THE EVOLUTION OF GENETICS

ACADEMIC PAPERBACKS*

EDITED BY Henry Booker, D. Allan Bromley, Nicholas DeClaris, W. Magnus, Alvin Nason, and A. Shenitzer

BIOLOGY

Design and Function at the Threshold of Life: The Viruses
HEINZ FRAENKEL-CONRAT
The Evolution of Genetics ARNOLD W. RAVIN
Isotopes in Biology GEORGE WOLF
Life: Its Nature, Origin, and Development A. I. OPARIN
Time, Cells, and Aging BERNARD L. STREHLER

ENGINEERING

A Vector Approach to Oscillations HENRY BOOKER
Dynamic Programming and Modern Control Theory RICHARD BELLMAN and ROBERT KALABA

MATHEMATICS

Finite Permutation Groups HELMUT WIELANDT
Elements of Abstract Harmonic Analysis GEORGE BACHMAN
The Method of Averaging Functional Corrections: Theory and Applications A. Yu. LUCHKA
Geometric Transformations (in two volumes) P. S. MODENOV and A. S. PARKHOMENKO
Representation Theory of Finite Groups MARTIN BURROW
Introduction to p-Adic Numbers and Valuation Theory
GEORGE BACHMAN
Linear Operators in Hilbert Space WERNER SCHMEIDLER
Noneuclidean Geometry HERBERT MESCHKOWSKI
Quadratic Forms and Matrices N. V. YEFIMOV

PHYSICS

Crystals: Their Role in Nature and in Science CHARLES BUNN
Elementary Dynamics of Particles H. W. HARKNESS
Elementary Plane Rigid Dynamics H. W. HARKNESS
Mössbauer Effect: Principles and Applications
GUNTHER K. WERTHEIM
Potential Barriers in Semiconductors B. R. GOSSICK
Principles of Vector Analysis JERRY B. MARION

*Most of these volumes are also available in a cloth bound edition.

THE EVOLUTION OF GENETICS

BY ARNOLD W. RAVIN

DEPARTMENT OF BIOLOGY
UNIVERSITY OF ROCHESTER
ROCHESTER, NEW YORK

ACADEMIC PRESS   New York and London

ACADEMIC PRESS INC.
111 Fifth Avenue, New York, New York 10003

United Kingdom Edition published by
ACADEMIC PRESS INC. (LONDON) LTD.
Berkeley Square House, London W.1

LIBRARY OF CONGRESS CATALOG CARD NUMBER: 65-18434

First Printing, 1965

Second Printing, 1966

PRINTED IN THE UNITED STATES OF AMERICA

To My Parents

PREFACE

The writing of this book has been prompted by the feeling that far-reaching discoveries in genetics have come so swiftly and furiously in the last two decades as to overwhelm most persons interested in the science of heredity, except perhaps for those actively engaged in genetic research. The impression is easily acquired that modern molecular genetics in particular, arose full-grown (seemingly out of the head of Zeus), dependent on little nourishment but that of the ingenuity and genius of its contemporary practitioners. In short, the debt of modern genetics to the past is easily overlooked, to the detriment of a proper appreciation of scientific continuity. Another impression created by our current successes suggests that the fundamental questions of heredity are all answered; there is little left to do, it seems, but to close shop and hunt for another field awaiting the kind of combined theoretical and experimental attack to which genetics gave way. On the contrary, it is the thesis of this book that, despite the rapidity of progress in contemporary genetic research, there is no danger of creating an arid field devoid of fruitful problems. Genetics has had a glorious past, an absorbing present, and promises to enjoy an exciting future. This book is not intended as a history of the science of heredity. By a brief and general survey, however, it seeks to show the connections of past to present research, and of current discoveries to future investigations.

What, indeed, has modern genetics been up to? What problems of heredity have been solved, and how did they receive their solution? This book is written for a broad audience interested in a general, not detailed, review of this subject. Undergraduates considering a career of teaching or research in biology, students who are embarking on graduate studies in biology, professional biologists working in fields other than genetics but interested in current research on heredity, and laymen who have had some education in biology and have a continued interest in biological science—all of these persons, it is hoped, may find something useful in this book. Genetics has had, and still has a unifying, central position in the biological sciences. Even more so in the future its principles will have ramifications in every specialized field of biology: biochemistry, physiology, cytology, development, systematics, ecology, and evolution. For this reason this book is especially directed toward the next generation of biological scientists, for they will bring the discoveries of modern genetics to bear on the difficult problems still confronting us at the frontiers of biology.

General as this survey will be, it will not be a leisurely journey requiring little active participation on the part of the reader. Rather, patient collaboration will be needed for the reader to gain a sufficiently clear view of both the well-mapped terrains and unexplored frontiers of modern genetics. To maintain an uninterrupted flow in the argument, specific references to the research literature have been avoided in the text. The reader wishing to probe more deeply into the topics discussed in the book may, nevertheless, consult the list of references.

The major part of this book was written while I was a visiting professor in the Department of Genetics of the University of California in Berkeley. I am grateful to my Berkeley colleagues for providing the unstrained ambiance in which this book could be conceived and fostered. I am also indebted to my colleagues in Rochester for their criticism of the early draft, and to my wife for help in developing a style and language appropriate to the task.

ARNOLD W. RAVIN

Rochester, New York
February, 1965

CONTENTS

THE LEGACY OF
CLASSICAL GENETICS

Biologists generally agree about the year of the birth of
the science of genetics. Prior to the work of Gregor Mendel
there existed no theoretical insight into the problems of
inheritance, no insight, at least, that could lend coherence
to the then existing experimental observations about animal
and plant breeding nor direction to further research. In the
middle of the nineteenth century, Mendel was crossing certain varieties of the pea plant in his monastery garden and
observing remarkable and reproducible patterns of transmission from one plant generation to the next. He took the
admirable step of furnishing an abstract, but experimentally
verifiable explanation of his findings, and his theoretical
contribution must be credited as having launched the new
biological discipline concerned with the transmission of
potentialities from parents to offspring. It was not until
1900, however, that biologists recognized, in what they did,
the significance of Mendel's contribution. The reasons for
this delay should prove a fertile subject for students of the
history of ideas, but we are concerned here with the dating
of an important event, the birth of genetics. Since 1900
marks the year when Mendel's ideas were put to further
tests by biologists, which resulted in the rapid development

1

of an enormously fruitful science (a development not yet come to term), genetics is recorded as having been born in that year. It is, consequently, a mere baby of a science, barely sixty-five years old.

It may be presumptuous to distinguish in so young a science a "classical" and a "modern" period. Yet the very speed with which genetic knowledge has expanded may account for the precocity with which fundamentally new ways of viewing things have succeeded each other in genetics. In any event, a significant change does seem to have come about in the way geneticists pose and attack questions. Early in the development of their discipline, geneticists treated the unit of inheritance, or gene, as a purely formal concept; their experiments consisted chiefly in analyzing the characteristics of *individuals* in order to determine the genetic constitutions (genotypes, or gene assemblages) of those individuals. In recent times—and it is difficult to say exactly when this change began—geneticists began explorations at higher and lower levels of organization than the individual. In descending to the molecular level, geneticists were concerned with the physiochemical nature of the gene, in order to deal with it less as a formal and abstract entity, and more as a material having physical and chemical properties that would account for its role in genetic transmission. At higher levels, geneticists interested in evolution began to analyze the genetic structure of populations, that is to say, the distributions of genotypes within populations. For evolution was seen to consist not in the evolution of *a* genotype, but in the evolution of genotypes which, through the individuals carrying them, interacted with each other and with the environment in complex ways.

While a date for the beginning of modern genetics cannot be set as easily as for the beginning of genetics itself, no one denies that the 1940's witnessed a tremendous rise in the molecular approach to gene structure and action. We can characterize roughly, therefore, a pre-1940 and a post-1940 genetics. Although we shall be considering in this book primarily the fruits of genetic investigations since 1940, there is no intention thereby either to dismiss or derogate the contributions of pre-1940 genetics. On the contrary, as is to be expected of the normal development of any science, a classical period sets the stage for the modern period. "Setting the stage" in a scientific context really means arriving at the right kinds of questions. With the advantage of historical perspective, we can see that classical genetics did just that. We can also see that it required special tools and particularly appropriate objects in order to answer the questions raised by the results of classical genetics. To approach the problems of gene structure and function, the essential tools were biochemical, and the especially suitable objects were microbial. On the other hand, the tools needed to study the structures of populations were largely mathematical.

A proper view of modern genetics would encompass the molecular approach to the gene and the populational approach to evolution. As a sign perhaps of the divergence and specialization within modern genetics, few books written today could be expected to represent fairly both approaches. This book will not be exceptional. Its aim, in any case, is limited; it is to survey what the molecular approach has managed to accomplish during the modern period of genetic research. Nevertheless, it will not leave evolutionary genetics entirely out of its range. Fortunately, connections with evolutionary genetics arise from considerations of the variations in genetic material, a topic to be examined in the final chapter.

It follows from what has already been said that one cannot safely ignore the legacy of classical genetics if one wants to understand why molecular genetics has pursued the particular course it has. Classical genetics gave direction to molecular genetics by posing certain basic questions. Let us review, therefore, in what must be a highly condensed fashion, the essential contributions of the classical period and the problems they raised.

The Concept of the Gene

Foremost among the accomplishments of classical genetics was the concept of a unit of inheritance, the *gene*. This contribution we owe, of course, to Mendel, and although molecular genetics has forced a critical reappraisal of this concept—and indeed has clarified our thinking while limiting our use of the concept—it seems fair to assert that genetic advance would have been unlikely without it.

In studying the appearance of parental characters in each new generation of garden pea plants, Mendel observed some very striking patterns of hereditary transmission. Mendel was certainly fortunate in possessing different varieties of the pea plant, varieties that differed from each other in some character such as seed color, seed shape, pod shape, or length of stem. Each of these characters exhibited alternative forms. Thus, for example, one variety bore exclusively green seeds; another bore exclusively yellow seeds. Moreover, each of these varieties bred true, which is to say that, if a plant exhibiting a certain character were self-fertilized, or were crossed with an identical plant, the progeny were all alike and similar to their parents. Without such true-breeding varieties, the kinds of experiments that Mendel subsequently performed would either be difficult or impossible to interpret.

The interesting experiments were, of course, those in which a true-breeding plant with one set of characteristics was crossed to a true-breeding plant with an alternative set of characteristics. A typical example is shown in Text Fig. 1, which summarizes the results of an experiment in which a true-breeding yellow-seeded plant is crossed to a true-breeding green-seeded plant. The rules of inheritance that were observed in these crosses are familiar to everyone who has studied biology, and they need only be summarized very briefly here. One of the alternative parental characters disappears in the first generation of offspring issuing from such a cross (called the first filial generation or F_1). However, the potentiality for producing the missing character is actually hidden or masked in the F_1 plants. This fact is demonstrated by crossing any two F_1 plants to produce a second filial generation, or F_2. Individuals possessing the character missing in the F_1 generation reappear in the F_2. Moreover, the plants with this character account for a

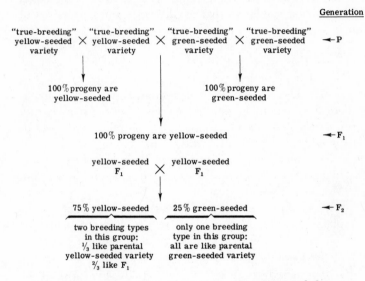

TEXT FIG. 1. The classic Mendelian cross: green-seededness vs. yellow-seededness in the garden pea plant. The outcome of these crosses is independent of whether the "true-breeding" yellow-seeded variety serves as the male or female parent in the original cross of the parental (P) generation. F_1 and F_2 refer, respectively, to the first and second filial generations.

remarkably reproducible fraction of the F_2 plants; one-quarter is generally the fraction of F_2 plants bearing the character that had disappeared in the F_1 generation. Another important rule concerned the F_2 plants exhibiting the character typical of the F_1 plants (yellow-seededness in the case schematized in Text Fig. 1). Not all of these plants were alike in breeding behavior; two-thirds of these plants behaved like their F_1 parents, while one-third were true-breeding and behaved in every respect like those plants in the original cross (or P generation) possessing the character that did not disappear in the F_1.

Mendel was not content merely to observe and to record these regular patterns of hereditary transmission. He proposed to explain the results, and in order to do so he acted in a manner similar to that of physicists and chemists who had before him accounted for certain regular features and orderly processes in nature by assuming the existence of entities that were not directly observable, but could be assigned hypothetical properties as to account for the observed order and regularity. The atom is, after all, a hypothetical construction and is endowed with precisely the properties it needs to explain the divisibility and electromagnetic properties of matter, the falling of chemical elements into groups according to their characteristic reactivity, the stoichiometry of chemical reactions, and so on.

Mendel's thinking was similar. He was prepared to invent an entity existing in living organisms that would explain heredity. Although he used a different name for this hypothetical unit, geneticists have subsequently applied to it the name *gene*. How did Mendel's gene work? In the first place, Mendel proposed that in the adult pea plant there were two genes, or *alleles*, determining the development of each recognizable hereditary character. Each of these alleles could exist in at least two alternative forms. If the two alleles were identical, the organism was true-breeding for the character in question and was referred to by geneticists as *homozygous*. If the two alleles were different, the organism was not true-breeding and was referred to as *heterozygous*. Mendel proposed that when the two alleles were different, one of them was *dominant* in its effect, i.e., in its control over the development of the character being studied. The other allele, consequently, was *recessive*; that is to say, it was masked, although present, in a heterozygous individual (*heterozygote*). Exception to the duality of the genetic system arose in the formation of the sex cells, or gametes, of the mature organism. Mendel postulated that the eggs or pollen (sperm cells, in the case of animals) were produced in such a way that the paired nature of the genes was abolished, and each gamete contained but a single representative of each gene pair. Mendel assumed further that when a heterozygous individual produced gametes, it produced an equal number of each possible type, namely the type bearing one allele and the type bearing the other. Still other assumptions, or invented properties of the hypothetical gene, were required. One had to assume that fertilization of female gametes by male gametes was a random affair, at least in respect to the allelic contents of those gametes. It made no difference to a female gamete containing a given allele whether it were fertilized by a male gamete containing the same allele or a different one; fertilizations were not selective in this sense. Finally, it was necessary to assume that all zygotes, regardless of genic constitution, had an equal probability of development—at least of developing to an age at which their characters could be scored by the geneticist.

Armed with these assumptions, Mendel could readily account for the results of the breeding experiments he had conducted with the pea plant. An examination of Text Fig. 2 shows how simply the results are explained when one applies Mendel's assumptions to his crosses.

Mendel also performed crosses in which the parental varieties differed by two, and even three characters. In these crosses, he observed that the genes determining different characters are inherited independently of each other. Thus, for example, if he crossed a yellow, smooth-seeded variety to a green, wrinkled-seeded variety, all of the F_1 progeny produced yellow, smooth seeds. This result was not unanticipated, since previous crosses involving seed texture showed that the allele controlling smoothness was dominant to the allele determining a wrinkled appearance, just as crosses involving seed color had shown that the allele con-

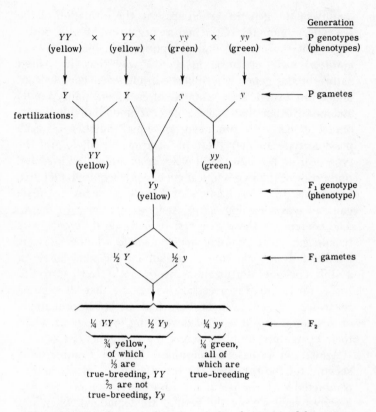

TEXT FIG. 2. Genic explanation of the classic Mendelian cross. Let $Y =$ allele determining yellow seed color, $y =$ allele determining green seed color, and Y be dominant over y. In the $F_1 \times F_1$ cross, fertilizations are assumed to occur at random. Therefore:

1. Probability a zygote will have genic constitution $YY =$ probability an egg contains $Y \times$ probability a male gamete contains $Y = 1/2 \times 1/2 = 1/4$.

2. Probability a zygote will have genic constitution $Yy =$ (probability an egg contains $Y \times$ probability a male gamete contains y) + (probability an egg contains $y \times$ probability a male gamete contains Y) = $(1/2 \times 1/2) + (1/2 \times 1/2) = 1/2$.

3. Probability a zygote will have genic constitution $yy =$ probability an egg contains $y \times$ probability a male gamete contains $y = 1/2 \times 1/2 = 1/4$.

trolling yellowness was dominant to the allele determining greenness. However, on crossing two of the F_1 progeny, not only did the recessive traits reappear, but some new combinations of characters were found. There were yellow, wrinkled-seeded plants and green, smooth-seeded plants in the F_2 generation, as well as the kinds of plants which were originally crossed in the parental P generation, namely, yellow, smooth-seeded and green, wrinkled-seeded plants. The proportions of the four kinds of F_2 plants revealed the independent transmission of the alleles for seed color and the alleles for seed shape: 9/16 of the F_2 were yellow, smooth-

Probability of single character arising in F_2 $\longrightarrow$		3/4 yellow	1/4 green $\longleftarrow$	seed color
3/4	smooth	yellow, smooth 9/16	green, smooth 3/16	
1/4	wrinkled	yellow, wrinkled 3/16	green, wrinkled 1/16	

seed texture

TEXT FIG. 3. Independent transmission of genes affecting different characters in the garden pea plant.

seeded; 3/16 were yellow, wrinkled-seeded; 3/16 were green, smooth-seeded; and 1/16 were green, wrinkled-seeded. If the two pairs of alleles were independently transmitted from the P to the F_2 generation, one would expect precisely this result. Consider Text Fig. 3, in which is listed the *probabilities* that any single parental character will appear in an F_2 plant as a consequence of the way in which the responsible allele is transmitted. From these one can calculate the probability of the coming-together, by chance, of any combination of parental characters, which is what independent transmission means in the present context. This probability is simply the product of the probabilities of appearance of the single characters. Thus, if the yellow-seeded character has a probability of 3/4 of developing in a given F_2 individual, and if the wrinkled-seeded appearance has a probability of 1/4 of arising in such an individual, the probability that these two characters will be present together in an F_2 plant will be given by $3/4 \times 1/4 = 3/16$. The results observed from the crosses involving multiple character differences were consistent with what Mendel expected on the basis of independently transmitted, nonallelic genes. Mendel, therefore, was led to believe that all combinations of characters were the result of the *fortuitous* segregation and reassortment of genes affecting different characters during gamete formation and fertilization.

Interaction of Alleles and of Nonallelic Genes

The triumph of classical genetics came not from the monotonous confirmation of Mendel's postulates in one organism after another, but rather from an astonishing series of complications and contradictions. Rather than demolish the hypothetical edifice constructed by Mendel, the post-1900 investigations had the effect of sifting the chaff from the kernels in Mendel's theory, of showing clearly what the essential common elements were in the genetic apparatus of all organisms. Incidentally, they also revealed just how complex the genetic machinery was in living things, how lucky Mendel was to investigate uncomplicated character differences in the pea plant, and how wise he was to exploit what he had, for as in all scientific progress, it is more likely that complicated truth will evolve from simplified, first approximations than simple truth from complicated hypotheses.

Among the properties assigned by Mendel to the genes and later found to be inconstant was the nature of the interaction between gene alleles. Dominance was not invariably the rule when one allele interacted with another in a given organism. Intermediate effects were produced sometimes, and whether or not one allele was completely dominant might be affected by the environment in which the organism developed, as well as by the kinds of other (nonallelic) genes present besides the allelic pair under analysis. This latter point is an example of one of the most important complications geneticists have had to cope with: the interaction of many nonallelic genes in the development of some character. Before discussing this point further, attention should be paid to the role of the environment which has just been briefly alluded to. Although classical genetics is sometimes criticized for suggesting genic autonomy in the control of developing characters (as, for example, by the Lysenkoist critics of "idealistic" genetics), one of the basic tenets of classical genetics is the ever-present interaction between the genetic constitution of the individual and his external environment. The assemblage of genes inherited by an individual from his parents *limits the potentialities* for development. The environment of the individual *elects* which of the potentialities will find manifest expression. To use an analogy originally proposed by Joshua Lederberg, and further extended by P. B. Medawar, the genotype is a set of genetic instructions for a limited number of alternative developmental pathways, but the particular pathway along which an individual is developing has been elected by the environment. The "gene vs. environment" or "nature vs. nurture" controversy is, in a general sense, fruitless, for it is impossible to suppress the role of either member of the postulated duality. It only becomes meaningful to inquire, in a specific instance, whether any conceivable environment can be found that will permit the development of some trait if given a certain genetic constitution to begin with—or whether any genetic constitution can be conceivably compounded that would permit the development of some character if given a particular environment to contend with. To express the genetic constitution of an individual, the geneticist uses the term *genotype*; for the specific group of characters that have in actuality been developed under the combined actions of genes and environment, the geneticist uses the term *phenotype*. The distinction was, in a sense, already made clear by Mendel, for he noted two different genotypes (one homozygous for a dominant gene allele, the other heterozygous for that allele) which brought about the same phenotype in a similar environment. Numerous instances may also be provided to demonstrate that identical genotypes operating within different environments may result in different phenotypes.

The opportunity that Mendel enjoyed to study the effects of single genes on certain characters was a happy one for the birth of genetics, but it cannot blind us to the fact that most characters, especially gross anatomical ones, are influenced by many nonallelic genes. In Mendel's work, the part contributed by a single gene to some character, like seed color, could be determined because the plants displaying a variation in that character differed only by an allelic change in a single gene. Heritable changes (called *mutations*) may arise, however, in other genes so as to cause changes in that same character. Thus, for example, seed color, in most plants, is the result of the interaction of many nonallelic genes, just as the coat color of mammals has been shown to be the product of the actions of several genes acting in concert. The interaction of several genes in determining a phenotypic character does not necessarily imply that these contribute to the character's production in exactly the same way. In regard to the coat color of mammals, some genes may affect the kinds of pigments synthesized by the animal, others may affect the quantities of pigments synthesized, still others may affect the distribution of the pigment and hence the pattern of the coat color, while others may affect different steps in the synthesis of some specific pigment.

The Relation of Gene to Character

As verifiable as the conclusion that different genes may impinge upon the same character is the conclusion that a single gene may contribute to more than one character. Examples abound, but one will suffice to illustrate the general situation. In the fruit fly *Drosophila*, a mutation may arise in a single gene to produce an allele having, in the homozygous state, one very dramatic and obvious effect, at least to the human observer: a large reduction in the size of the wings. Such a condition, known as "vestigial wings," renders the fly incapable of flight and, thereby, provides a striking phenotypic marker of the recessive allele in its homozygous state. If one studies other anatomical and physiological features of such a fly during the course of its development, one may note other, perhaps less obvious, but nevertheless significant changes from the normal condition. The vestigial-winged flies have altered bristles on their backs, the sperm-storing organs in the female are changed in shape, the number of egg strings produced in the ovaries is affected, and finally, these flies have a decreased longevity, and their reproductive ability is less than that of normal flies. Thus the mutated gene expresses itself in manifold ways during the complex processes of development.

Such manifold effects of the gene, often referred to as *pleiotropy*, and the intervention of numerous genes in any specific developmental process one may care to examine raise the question of the specificity of gene action. In brief, can one identify any primary activity of a gene as uniquely its own? After all, a unique activity of the gene is consistent with its pleiotropic effects, for the latter may be considered to be the by-products of the specific primary activity. Metabolism and development being complex, consisting as they do of intricate connections between numerous individual biochemical reactions and processes, a change in a single reaction may lead to several subsequent effects, each of which is traceable to and hence dependent upon the primarily affected reaction.

A schematic diagram of the relation of hypothetical primary gene activities to complex metabolic and developmental processes is given in Text Fig. 4. A mutation of gene *A* that would result in the disappearance or impairment of α, the primary product of gene *A*'s activity, would cause a change in the three characters w, x, and y. Similarly, if gene A were unchanged and actively producing α, but if gene D were mutated so that a defective δ were produced, characters x and y would both be affected. Thus, both the pleiotropy and interaction of genes could be accounted for on the basis of specific activities of the different genes.

While it is easy to construct such hypothetical schemes, it is difficult to identify the primary products of the genes. Although the search for the gene's primary product has

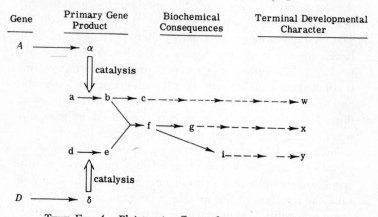

TEXT FIG. 4. Pleiotropic effects of unique gene actions.

been a characteristic feature of modern molecular genetics, classical genetic studies went very far in suggesting where one might look for this hypothetical product. A powerful hint was provided as early as 1905, in the pioneering work of Garrod in the field of human genetics. There are certain human metabolic diseases attributable to recessive alleles of single genes which are inherited in a strictly Mendelian fashion. One such disease is alcaptonuria, sufferers of which excrete a urine having the peculiarly striking feature of turning black on exposure to air. Garrod showed that alcaptonurics (homozygous for the recessive allele) possess this trait because they accumulate a substance, homogentisic acid, in their blood and eventually in their urine. On exposure to air, homogentisic acid is slowly oxidized to a dark product. Homogentisic acid is not accumulated in the blood of normal individuals, although it is an intermediate product of the oxidation of a normally occurring amino acid, phenylalanine. Homogentisic acid is converted by normal individuals into maleylacetoacetic acid which, in turn, is converted to simpler substances. The blood of normal persons contains an enzyme capable of catalyzing the conversion of homogentisic acid into maleylacetoacetic acid; the blood of alcaptonurics, on the other hand, lacks an enzyme with such activity. Therefore, it is reasonable to suppose that the recessive allele responsible for alcaptonuria is deficient in a specific activity, which the normal allele carries out. This activity is manifested in the production of the enzyme having homogentisic acid as its substrate. Is the enzyme the primary product of this gene? About this question, more will be said later. For now, let it suffice to recognize that, during the classical period, the effects of certain genes were already being studied at the molecular level, where it was possible to do so in several different organisms. In many of these cases, the effects of individual genes were traceable to specific enzymes; gene mutations, in other words, were often found to result in absent or inactive enzymes—the particular enzyme affected being characteristic of a particular gene. If specific enzymes, which are known to catalyze specific biochemical reactions, are substituted for the specific primary gene products shown in Text Fig. 4, an interpretation can be provided for pleiotropy, gene interaction, and specific gene activity in terms of known biological molecules, the enzymes. How well this interpretation fits our present understanding of gene function must be left for extended treatment in Chapter V.

Localization of the Gene on the Chromosome

The most glaring contradiction to Mendel's rules, however, arose with the observation that nonallelic genes are not always transmitted independently of each other. The contradiction led to our knowledge of where the gene resides in the living cell and, eventually, to an appreciation of the chemical nature of the gene.

Interestingly enough, the nonindependent transmission of certain genes was predicted in advance of its observation. We owe this insight to Walter Sutton, who was studying spermatogenesis (male gametogenesis) in the grasshopper at the turn of the century in Columbia University. Sutton had been aware of the rediscovery and belated appreciation, in the year 1900, of Mendel's researches originally published in 1866. He was also aware of the conclusions that he and several of his predecessors had reached concerning the manner in which *chromosomes* behave during cell reproduction. These conclusions, based on studies with plant and animal cells of many different species, had certain common features:

1. The cells of a given species of organism possess a characteristic number of filamentous structures, the chromosomes, which are located in the nucleus.

2. The chromosomes in cells other than the gametes consist of pairs of recognizably distinct morphological types; that is, there are usually two of each kind of chromosome in a given cell nucleus.

3. When cells reproduce, the chromosomes are reproduced and equitably distributed to the daughter cells, so that every cell produced by this process of *mitosis* contains two copies of each kind of chromosome.

4. One notable exception, however, is observed during the special process of cell reproduction known as *meiosis*; in this case, the daughter cells receive only one copy of each kind of chromosome; the daughter cells arising from meiosis are the future gametes that participate in fertilization.

5. Fertilization of the female gamete by the male gamete gives rise to a single-celled zygote, the nucleus of which again contains the chromosomes in a paired condition; the zygote reproduces by mitosis, and it gradually develops into an adult individual of the next generation.

Sutton perceived that the chromosomes are *observed* to behave precisely the way Mendel's genes are *postulated* to behave. The chromosomes and genes are both paired in the adult individual, reduced to the unpaired condition in the gamete, and restored to the paired condition again in the zygote. (The terms *diploid* and *haploid* are used to express, respectively, the paired and unpaired states of the chromosomes and the genes.) What could be simpler than to imagine that the gene is carried on the chromosome, and the postulated behavior of the gene in inheritance is a reflection of the mechanics of chromosome transmission from one generation to the next? Sutton also realized that certain consequences followed from this conception. Either the chromosomes are equivalent to genes, or the genes are components of the chromosome. If the former were true, the number of genes available to an organism would be equal to the haploid number of chromosomes. Since the haploid number of chromosomes in certain organisms is quite small (2 in the horse worm *Ascaris*, 4 in the fruit fly *Drosophila melanogaster*, 7 in the rye plant), and the number of non-allelic genes in a given organism is surely at least on the order of hundreds, it follows that genes must be parts of chromosomes and, moreover, that *certain genes must be associated on the same chromosome*. In this way, the physical linkage of certain groups of genes was predicted.

Sutton's insight was published in 1903. In the exciting years that followed, his hypothesis was established as its predictions were confirmed. Working in Columbia University's laboratories of zoology, where Sutton had been a student, were T. H. Morgan and a group of his collaborators, A. H. Sturtevant, C. B. Bridges, and H. J. Muller. They were largely responsible for establishing the chromosomal theory of inheritance as it is referred to today. An important result of their work was the demonstration that certain genes are linked. It may be helpful to illustrate how this was shown.

The fruit fly *Drosophila melanogaster* could be cultivated

from fertilized egg to adulthood in the laboratory. Certain rare flies were found to possess characters different from the normal, or *wild-type* variety. These differences were, moreover, heritable, and shown often to be due to recessive alleles of dominant, wild-type genes: a cross between mutant and wild-type flies gave the usual Mendelian 3:1 ratio in the F_2 progeny. Certain pairs of genes were transmitted independently of each other, as Mendel had found. Other gene pairs were transmitted in a different manner. Consider, for example, the case of the mutant character called *black body* because of the characteristic pigmentation associated with the mutant fly. It was inherited in a normal Mendelian manner, as was the character called *vestigial*, which has previously been referred to in connection with pleiotropy. If one crossed a black, normal-winged fly with a normally pigmented, vestigial-winged fly, the F_1 generation consisted of flies that were all alike, flies that were normal in wing and body pigmentation. Quite unexpected results were obtained, however, on crossing the F_1 flies—unexpected, that is, on the assumption that the genes affecting body color and wing shape were independently transmitted (i.e., genetically unlinked). The nature of the difficulty is made clear on examining the results of crossing an F_1 female* with a doubly recessive male. As may be seen in Text Fig. 5, four possible phenotypic combinations may be expected among the progeny of this test cross. Two phenotypic combinations must be due to a *recombination* in the F_1 gametes of the wild-type and mutant alleles, respectively, of the genes affecting body color and wing shape; these recombinant phenotypes are *wild type* and *doubly mutant*. The other two phenotypes, *black body* + *normal wing* and *normal body* + *vestigial wing*, are due to combinations of the alleles in the F_1 gametes like those of the parental generation, and hence they are called parental combina-

---

* A technical reason makes it necessary to use an F_1 female. Recombination of linked genes does not occur in the *Drosophila* male, which adds another complication we can dispense with for the present.

tions. If the genes affecting wing shape and body color were transmitted independently of each other, there should be equal proportions of the parental and recombinant gametes produced by the F_1 female, and consequently there should

P Generation:

Phenotype:	black body, normal wing	×	normal body, vestigial wing
Genotype:	b/b , +/+		+/+ , v/v
Gamete type:	b , +		+ , v

F_1 Generation:

Phenotype: normal body , normal wing
Genotype: b/+ , +/v

Test Cross: F_1 (female) × black body, vestigial wing (male)

Possible gametic types: recombinant $\begin{cases} +, + \\ b, v \end{cases}$ b , v

parental gametes $\begin{cases} +, v \\ b, + \end{cases}$

			Proportions	
Test cross progeny:	Genotypes	Phenotypes	Expected	Observed
	+/b , +/v	normal body, normal wing	0.25	0.085
	b/b , v/v	black body, vestigial wing	0.25	0.085
	+/b , v/v	normal body, vestigial wing	0.25	0.415
	b/b , +/v	black body, normal wing	0.25	0.415

TEXT FIG. 5. Linked transmission of genes affecting different characters in the fruit fly. Proportions in the test cross progeny shown as expected are calculated on the assumption that the genes are not linked (i.e., are transmitted independently).

be equal proportions of the parental and recombinant phenotypes among the offspring of this test cross. (Since the doubly mutant male used in the test cross can produce only one type of gamete, the various possibilities are relatively easy to determine.) The results actually obtained are at variance with this expectation. The two recombinant phenotypes are produced, and they are equally frequent *relative to each other*, but the total number of flies having the recombinant characters constitutes a small minority compared to the total number of flies possessing the parental characters. It follows that the genes affecting body color and wing shape may be recombined, but there is some barrier to recombination. The parental combinations of genes tend to persist on transmission to the next generation; they are *genetically linked*.

The frequency of recombinant progeny issuing from the test cross is remarkably constant under fixed experimental conditions. Moreover, if one performs the experiment starting with a wild-type parent and a doubly mutant parent, the results of the test cross are again parental types in the majority of test cross progeny, and recombinant types in the minority. This time, however, the recombinant types are *black body + normal wing* and *normal body + vestigial wing*, but their numbers are equal to the numbers of recombinant progeny in the previous set of crosses. Therefore, the frequency of recombination of nonallelic genes is independent of the allelic state of the genes entering into the parental cross.

Certain genes are clearly linked in inheritance, as Sutton predicted, but the linkage is not absolute or complete; linked genes may recombine. Genes affecting other phenotypic characters of the fruit fly are found to be linked to the genes affecting body color and wing shape that have just been described. However, each pair of linked genes undergoes recombination with a constant frequency characteristic of the pair; for some pairs, the recombination frequency is relatively high, for others, relatively low. A further interesting property of recombination is soon realized: the recombination frequencies of linked genes are approximately additive. Thus, if gene A (affecting some character a) is found to be linked to genes B and C (affecting characters b and c, respectively), the frequency of recombination between genes A and C turns out to be either the sum or the difference of the B-C and A-B recombination frequencies. What is the meaning of this additivity of recombination frequencies? By hypothesis, genes linked to each other are carried on the same chromosome. One may account for the characteristic frequency of recombination between a given pair of linked genes by assuming that the *distance* between the genes determines the frequency of recombination; the greater the distance is, the greater the opportunity is for recombination. Of course, some model of recombination between linked genes must be invoked here. One possible model starts with the directly observable fact that, at an early stage of meiosis, similar (*homologous*) chromosomes come together in a fairly exact fashion, placing in apposition the genes on one chromosome with their homologous counterparts on the other chromosome. If, at this stage of intimate pairing (or *synapsis*) between homologous chromosomes, physical exchanges took place as shown in Text Fig. 6, recombination of linked genes would be the outcome. According to this model, the chance that an exchange will take place within a given region of the chromosome would be greater the larger the region. Therefore, the probability that two genes are contained in the same chromosomal region undergoing exchange would be an inverse function of the distance between the genes; distant genes would be separated by recombination more frequently than very close ones. This suggested model of recombination assumes that physical exchanges occur during the meiotic stage when homologous chromosomes are observed, under the ordinary light microscope, to be closely synapsed; this assumption about the *time* of exchange may, in fact, be wrong. Nevertheless, whatever the *physical* basis of recombination between linked genes, the observed additivity of recombination frequencies permits one to express linkage relationships in terms of genetic distances. (In actuality, it is known that genetic distances do not correspond exactly to physical distances.) Indeed, geneticists construct linear maps showing the genetic distances between linked genes, using as a unit of genetic distance the Morgan unit, which corresponds to a frequency of one recombination between the pair of genes in question per 100 gametes produced. Such a map is shown in Text Fig. 7, which illustrates the approximate additivity of the genetic distances between a group of *Drosophila* genes to which *black* and *vestigial* belong.

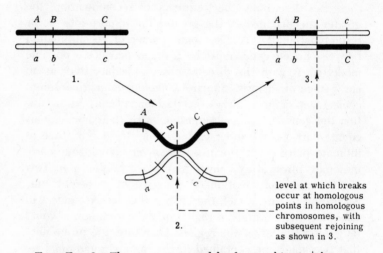

level at which breaks occur at homologous points in homologous chromosomes, with subsequent rejoining as shown in 3.

TEXT FIG. 6. The cross-over model of recombination between linked genes. For the sake of simplicity, the cross-over is drawn as occurring between two single-stranded chromosomes. In actuality, it is known that each chromosome consists of two sister strands at the time cross-overs take place. Therefore, a cross-over must occur between nonsister strands of bipartite chromosomes. Genetic evidence for cross-overs at the "four-strand stage" consists in the finding that the tetrad of gametes produced by meiosis generally contains two parental and two recombinant chromosomes for a given pair of genes.

If it seems that the picture of recombination between linked genes is based on many assumptions and, therefore, fraught with uncertainties, this is because our understanding of the mechanism of recombination is far from clear. This is a problem requiring further efforts by cytologists and molecular geneticists. Because it remains a vexing problem during a period of genetic research in which many other

Mutant	Symbol	Map position	Normal
aristaless (short aristae)	al	0	long aristae
dumpy wings	dp	3.0	long wings
short legs (four tarsi)	d	31.0	long legs (five tarsi)
black body	b	48.5	gray body
purple eyes	pr	54.5	red eyes
vestigial wings	vg	67.0	long wings
curved wings	c	75.5	straight wings
bent wings	a	99.2	straight wings
brown eyes	bw	104.0	red eyes

TEXT FIG. 7. A portion of the genetic map of chromosome II of *Drosophila melanogaster*. The phenotypes produced by gene mutations on chromosome II of *Drosophila melanogaster* are shown above the line; the normal phenotypes are shown below the line. The genetic symbols for the mutations are indicated immediately above the sites where the mutations are mapped. Thus the symbol *vg* stands for "vestigial wings." Immediately below the line are indicated the cross-over distances of the corresponding mutant sites from the left-hand extremity of the chromosome. Thus, the frequency of recombination between *al* and *d* (31%) is about equal to the recombination frequency between *d* and *vg* (36%), and therefore the map distances from *al* to *d* and from *d* to *vg* are shown as nearly equal. From E. Altenburg, "Genetics." Holt, Rinehart & Winston, New York, 1957.

problems are apparently being nicely solved, recombination deserves more attention, and we will return to it in Chapter IV. Yet classical genetics *did* settle at least two important matters. First of all, innumerable predictions of the chromosomal theory of genetic transmission have been confirmed, so that there is no doubt today about its validity. One confirmed prediction is that, in species adequately studied genetically, the number of groups of linked genes should be equal to the haploid number of chromosomes. Another prediction is that the pattern of a gene's transmission from one generation to the next should reflect any abnormality or special property of the chromosome carrying the gene. In many sexually reproducing species, one pair of chromosomes is exceptional, in that the members of the pair are not exactly homologous morphologically or in genic contents. This is the well known X-Y pair of sex chromosomes. This pair is found in only one of the sexes (in males among humans), while a homologous X-X pair is found in the other sex (in human females). The Y chromosome behaves as though it lacked certain genes present on the X chromosome. The essential point, in brief, is that the pattern of transmission of X-borne genes to male and female individuals is exactly predictable. Since human males get their X chromosomes only from their mothers, any recessive X-linked heterozygosity of the mother is revealed by the phenotypes of one-half of her sons. Still another exceptional situation that proves the rule is that of *nondisjunction*. Occasionally homologous chromosomes do not separate or disjoin during meiosis, so that rare gametes possess two copies of one of the chromosome types. This situation is cytologically demonstrable, which makes it possible to show that the exceptional nondisjunction is always accompanied by a predictable change in genotype.

Another important matter settled during the classical period is that recombination between linked genes is accompanied by a physical exchange between chromosomes. (Incidentally, it seems obvious that such a demonstration is in further support of the theory that chromosomes are the vehicles of genes.) To prove this point, Curt Stern performed an elegant experiment which took advantage of another rare occurrence in chromosomes. Occasionally, chromosomes break, and the frequency of such breakage can actually be increased with the use of ionizing radiation. Broken chromosomes tend to heal by rejoining and reestablishing their initial configurations. However, if the broken fragments get far enough apart, they may unite with other, nonhomologous chromosomes which may also have become broken and have exposed, unhealed ends. New, readily recognizable chromosome types, called *translocations*, are thus produced. A gene that is on a translocated piece should have

---

TEXT FIG. 8. Correlation of chromosomal exchanges with genetic recombinations. These diagrams summarize Stern's experiment. *B* stands for a dominant mutation (*Bar*) causing reduced eye size; *car* stands for a recessive mutation (*carnation*) causing, in the homozygous state, an abnormal carnation coloration of the eye; + stands for the normal, or wild-type, allele of each gene. These two mutations occur on the X chromosome. In I are shown the results of crossing-over between *Bar* and *carnation* in a female that has normal X chromosomes. In II are shown the results in a female in which the X chromosomes have undergone changes due to translocations. In the latter female, one X chromosome is J-shaped because a fragment of the Y chromosome is translocated to a position near one of the ends (the end indicated by an open circle in the diagrams); the other X chromosome has lost a fragment, not containing the *Bar* and *carnation* sites, which has been translocated to one of the fourth chromosomes. In the diagrams, only the X chromosomes are shown. The important point of the experiment is that in I, crossing-over results in no cytological change, whereas in II, crossing-over results in chromosomes morphologically different from noncrossover chromosomes. By using a homozygous carnation-eyed male as a tester, the genetically recombinant progeny (those with reduced eyes of normal color and those with normal-sized eyes of carnation color) can be distinguished. They are found to have the predicted types of recombinant chromosomes, when the female parent is of the type shown in II. Modified from R. King, "Genetics." Oxford Univ. Press, London and New York, 1962.

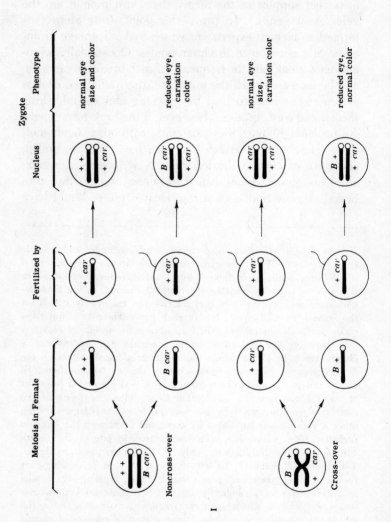

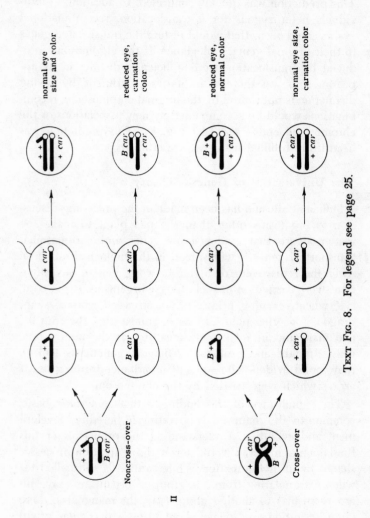

TEXT FIG. 8. For legend see page 25.

new allegiances in terms of the genes to which it is linked. This prediction was quickly confirmed. In addition, in individuals heterozygous for a translocation, recombinational events could occur that would restore the translocated genes to their original genetic allegiance. If the chromosome produced by translocation were sufficiently distinct in its appearance, as was the case in Stern's experiment, by having distinct ends not shared by the original chromosome, recombinations would be accompanied by new associations of the chromosome ends (see Text Fig. 8). This prediction was beautifully fulfilled in Stern's experiments.

The Universality of Genetic Theory

Sufficient allusion has been made in the preceding discussion to organisms other than the pea plant to make the reader aware that evidence for genes and chromosomal transport of genes is widespread in the biological universe. After the rediscovery of Mendel's work, genetic investigations were carried on in such diverse organisms as the corn, rye, wheat, evening primrose, jimson weed, cotton, snapdragon, and other plants, in mice, guinea pigs, the fruit fly, and man, and in such lowly creatures as the microscopic yeasts, molds, and protozoa. Wherever geneticists looked, they found evidence for units of inheritance forming linear arrays which were carried by the chromosomes.

The significance of this finding is that something basic, common to all organisms, is operating in heredity, development and evolution. Understanding the properties of this fundamental material would surely throw light on processes shared by all living matter. While caution is still called for when extrapolating from one group of organisms (say, microorganisms) to another group (say, the mammals), there is no hesitation any longer about using a particular group of organisms to attack a fundamental problem of genetics, if these organisms are advantageous for the investigations of interest.

A Genetic Theory of Evolution

The universal applicability of genetic theory has especially encouraged a theoretical approach to the phenomenon of biological evolution. In evolution we witness the heritable changes in organisms, and groups of organisms, in time. While Darwin was not aware of the source of heritable variations, nor more particularly of their manner of transmission through successive generations, he realized that heritable changes must be available as the raw materials on which natural selection could act and weed out poorly fit types.

The first important contribution of genetics to evolutionary biology was the demonstration of units of inheritance and precise mechanisms of their transmission. A theory of evolution could now be placed on a rigorous, mathematical basis. Helpful in this regard was the realization of a significant property of genes: alleles of a gene do not blend or contaminate each other in the heterozygous individual, so that the character differences they determine reappear in subsequent generations. G. H. Hardy and W. Weinberg deduced the mathematical consequence of such a nonblending system of heredity. The mathematical consequence (or Hardy-Weinberg law, as it is called) is that the frequency of a given gene allele in a population of interbreeding individuals tends to remain constant through successive generations. More precisely, the relative proportions of the alleles of any gene, in the population at large, remain the same in each generation *unless* certain forces intervene to change them. Genetical research into evolutionary processes consists in finding out just what those forces are and what their relative strengths are in particular situations, since evolution must consist in the change of gene frequencies.

One may grasp intuitively that mutation, genetic recombination, and natural selection are effective agencies in evolution. After all, mutation causes gene changes, and recombination assembles various combinations of genes. Because the individual organisms possessing these different gene combinations do not have the same ability to survive and reproduce, certain gene combinations become more frequent in the population, others less so. This is what is meant by natural selection. Mathematical models employing these evolutionary agencies take us much further than intuition, however. They make possible predictions of the rate with which certain genotypes will wax or wane in the population, given the rates of mutation, the survival and reproductive values of particular genotypes, and such other factors as the size of the interbreeding population and the rate of migration into or out of the population. Experimental populations may be set up with initial values for certain of these parameters, and one may examine how genotypic frequencies fluctuate as new generations come forth. In this way the mathematical models of evolution may be tested. Originally inspired by the notable contributions of R. A. Fisher, J. B. S. Haldane, and Sewall Wright, efforts along such avenues of research are continuing today. Although currently attracting less fanfare and excitement than herald the accomplishments of molecular genetics, it may be expected that powerful new ideas and fruitful hypotheses will be forthcoming from this challenging field.

The Role of the Cytoplasm in Heredity

The importance of the chromosomal genes in heredity sometimes causes us to conceive of the cytoplasm as a labile matrix on which the genes impart their directive influence. The cytoplasm, in this view, is a field having a structure and function regulated exclusively by the nucleus. Classical genetics has, in fact, proved this simple view to be incorrect. There is little doubt, of course, that the chromosomally located genes carry hereditary information concerning much of the cell's vital functions. Nevertheless, experimental results have established that the nucleus does not enjoy exclusive control in this regard.

There is a large variety of cytoplasmic organelles, which are distinguishable from each other by morphological appearance, as well as biochemical specialization. These organelles include the ribosomes, the mitochondria, the Golgi apparatus, and in green plant cells, the chloroplasts. The mitochondria contain a very important part of the energy-releasing and energy-transferring enzymes contained in the cell. The ribosomes, as will be later amplified, are primarily involved in protein synthesis. The chloroplasts contain the photosynthetic machinery of the green plant. It is entirely conceivable, of course, that the molecular contents of all of these cytoplasmic organelles are determined by the genetic information contained in the cell's chromosomes. We know, however, that this cannot be entirely true. Since 1910, it has been known that mutations may cause defects in the photosynthetic apparatus of green plants. One such mutation is characterized by "albino" (chlorophyll-less) chloroplasts. The seat of this mutation turns out not to be a chromosomal gene, but a hereditary determinant located within the chloroplast itself, for the albino character can be shown to depend not on the source of the cell's nucleus, but on the source of the cell's cytoplasm. Indeed, albino chloroplasts reproduce albino chloroplasts, just as normal, green chloroplasts reproduce green chloroplasts.

Similarly, in yeast cells, a mutation may occur in some cytoplasmic organelle, possibly in the mitochondrion or its precursor, and cause a deficiency in the system of energy release and transport in the cell. The cell is deficient in this metabolic function if its cytoplasm consists mainly of the mutated cytoplasmic determinants; the nucleus of a deficient cell relocated in a normal cytoplasm does not cause any subsequent abnormality. On the other hand, if the cell is deficient, it will remain so whether a nucleus from a normal or a deficient cell is substituted into it.

Thus, the cytoplasm makes a definite contribution to the hereditary repertoire of the cell. The relative contributions of the nucleus and the cytoplasm perhaps cannot be accurately assayed, at least with present methods, because of the disparity in the number of copies of the nuclear and cytoplasmic determinants within the cell. In a diploid cell, the number of chromosomal genes having a specific function is 2; in a haploid cell, it is only one. Regardless of the chromosomal ploidy, however, the number of cytoplasmic determinants having a specific function in the cell may be quite large. If there were as few as one determinant per organelle, the number of determinants would still be large, since the number of organelles per cell is large; there are at least hundreds of mitochondria per cell, for example. Consequently, in order to learn of a cytoplasmic determinant serving a specific hereditary function, one must detect it in a mutated form, and the mutant phenotype may only be expressed if a large majority of the specific determinants within the cell were mutated. Such a situation may not often arise, and therefore the existence of cytoplasmic determinants with hereditary functions may be difficult to detect. It is little wonder that geneticists have concentrated their attention on nuclear genes.

The Questions Raised by Classical Genetics

Admittedly the foregoing has been an extremely condensed and highly abbreviated review of the classical period of genetic research. Nevertheless, it will have served our present purposes if it has made evident the fundamental questions that were posed for the geneticists of the modern period:

1. What is the gene?
2. How does it work to determine the development of characters? What is the relative part played by cytoplasmic determinants in the development of characters?
3. How is the gene disposed on the chromosome, and how does recombination occur between linked genes?
4. How does the gene and the genotype change, and how do populations evolve and new species arise?

The remainder of this book will be concerned with the contributions of molecular genetics toward the solution of these questions. We shall see that there have been remarkable successes along with unfulfilled hopes.

CHAPTER II

THE USE OF MICROORGANISMS IN MOLECULAR GENETICS

For almost any kind of genetic research, one would like to use organisms that are easy to cultivate, reproduce rapidly, and are small enough so that very large numbers of them can be contained in a small volume. Microorganisms ideally meet these criteria. They are small, ranging in size from a micron in diameter for the bacteria to a few microns in diameter for the filaments of molds (one micron is equal to 1/10,000 of a centimeter). They are easily grown in either liquid or solid media, the constituents of which are often fairly simple and easy to reproduce. The liquid medium in which *Escherichia coli,* the intestinal bacterium, can be grown consists of a sugar, such as glucose, plus phosphate, sulfate, nitrate, and chloride salts of potassium, sodium, magnesium, and ammonium dissolved in water. Inoculated into such a medium, a few invisible bacteria will reproduce by growth and fission to give rise to visible clouds teeming with billions of individually invisible bacteria. A solid medium is sometimes useful, and it is obtained by adding an inert substance, agar, which causes the medium to form a gel. On the surface of solid medium, a single bacterium or yeast will give rise to a visible colony, formed by the piling up of the millions of descendants which stay in place (unless the bacteria are motile) (see Plate 1).* The filamentous molds grow somewhat differently, producing a loose, interlaced mesh of long, continuous filamentous strands. This meshwork is referred to as the mycelium, and the strands are the hyphae, which grow by prolongation. Inside the hyphae of certain molds, the nuclei reproduce without being separated by cytoplasmic cross-walls, so that many nuclei may share a common cytoplasm. The microorganisms reproduce rapidly. A single *E. coli* bacterium will undergo fission to produce two daughter bacteria every 20 to 30 minutes, according to the temperature and other conditions prevailing in the medium. The mycelial frontier of a filamentous mold such as *Neurospora crassa* will advance about 4 mm every hour. For these reasons alone, geneticists might have turned to microorganisms as objects for investigation. Fortunately, the microorganisms are also an excellent material for biochemical studies. Their small size and rapid rate of reproduction make it possible to obtain a large amount of material in a brief period of time. The preciseness with which one can control the external environment of the microorganism is reflected in a rather good homogeneity in the chemical constitutions of these organisms. Finally, they are relatively simple to break open so that their contents are readily extractable, separated, and purified.

Molecular Specificity and Organization within the Cell

The combined advantages in using microorganisms both for biochemical and genetic purposes cannot be overemphasized, for as we have just seen, the problems of heredity are posable in molecular terms. What is the physicochemical nature of the gene? How does this nature express itself in directing the metabolic activity of the cell in which it re-

---

* Plates 1 to 6 have been grouped together following page 54.

sides? The rise of molecular genetics—the attack of genetic questions at the molecular level—came not only when geneticists were asking such questions, but also when prior biochemical research had already provided much knowledge about the metabolic events occurring in the cells of organisms. Without going into details, which may be consulted in suitable texts, the basic discoveries may be summarized as follows:

1. *Energy release and coupling to energy-consuming reactions.*

In the oxidation of organic compounds within the cell, energy is released in a form that is not entirely lost to the environment. An important portion of the energy produced by oxidation is incorporated in chemically bonding a phosphate moiety to a fragment of the oxidized compound. In this way, the high energy bond of the phosphate moiety is available for utilization in reactions that require energy. However, this bond energy is first stored in a molecule of adenosine triphosphate (ATP). Thus, if X is allowed to symbolize some organic compound and P a phosphate moiety, if ADP and ATP represent adenosine di- and triphosphate, respectively, and the symbols — and ~ represent, respectively, low and high energetic levels of chemical bonding, the reactions leading to the storage of chemical energy may be represented as follows:

$$X + P \longrightarrow X - P \xrightarrow{\text{oxidation}} Y \sim P + Z$$
$$Y \sim P + ADP \longrightarrow Y + ATP \text{ (or } ADP \sim P\text{)}$$

The ATP thus produced is called upon by numerous energy-consuming reactions in the cell, and among the most important of these reactions are those of biosynthesis, namely, the reactions which synthesize the metabolically active reagents of the cell. An example is the synthesis of an important class of compounds, the proteins. In this process, the constituents of proteins, or amino acids, are joined together, and a class of substances, the soluble ribonucleic acids, or sRNA, transport the amino acids to large particles, the ribosomes, where the joining takes place. Considering for the moment only two amino acids, aa_1 and aa_2, the process may be represented as follows, in which the energy contained within ATP is eventually utilized in joining the two amino acids:

I.
$$aa_1 + ATP \longrightarrow aa_1 \sim AMP + PP$$
(adenosine   (pyrophosphate)
monophosphate)

$$aa_1 \sim AMP + sRNA_1 \longrightarrow aa_1 \sim sRNA_1 + AMP$$

II.
$$aa_2 + ATP \longrightarrow aa_2 \sim AMP + PP$$
$$aa_2 \sim AMP + sRNA_2 \longrightarrow aa_2 \sim sRNA_2 + AMP$$

III. $$aa_1 \sim sRNA_1 + aa_2 \sim sRNA_2 \xrightarrow{\text{ribosomes}}$$
$$aa_1 \sim aa_2 + sRNA_1 + sRNA_2$$

2. *Chains of biochemical reactions and interactions.*

As may be surmised from the preceding discussion of energy release and coupling, metabolic events are complex. A good deal of the complexity is due to the fact that such over-all processes as carbohydrate oxidation or amino acid synthesis are, in reality, composed of a large number of discrete steps. One step furnishes a compound which can then be utilized in the next step, so that a chain of biochemical reactions results. Connections between different reaction chains arise also when the product of one reaction serves as substrate for reactions in two different chains. An abstract version of a typical reaction sequence may be indicated as follows:

$$A \longrightarrow B \longrightarrow C \longrightarrow D ------\to aa_1$$
$$M \longrightarrow N \longrightarrow O \longrightarrow P ------\to aa_2$$

3. *Induction of biochemical reactions.*

There is a remarkable regulation of the economy of the cell, such that certain reactions are induced only under specific conditions. The agents promoting biochemical reactions in the cell are proteinaceous substances known as enzymes; these biocatalysts are not always being synthesized, even in cells possessing the genetic capacity to synthesize them. A common condition for the synthesis of an enzyme is the appearance of the specific substance convertible by the enzyme. Thus, an enzyme's substrate is often the *inducer* of the enzyme's synthesis. The enzyme's synthesis is suppressed in the absence of the substrate, *induced* in its presence. Similarly, the enzyme's synthesis can often be blocked by some eventual product in the chain of events promoted by the enzyme; repression of enzyme synthesis usually occurs if the product, called a repressor, reaches too high a concentration within the cell. Thus, enzymes that are not needed, either because their substrates are absent or products are accumulating, cease to be synthesized, entailing a net saving in energy and raw materials to the cell.

4. *Cell constituents possessing chemical specificity.*

Enzymes catalyze biochemical reactions, and they are fairly discriminating in what they catalyze. A given enzyme catalyzes usually but a small set of reactions, usually but one in the intact cell. An enzyme is said, in this regard, to be specific, and its specificity resides in a unique structure. Other classes of substances having this same feature of specificity are produced in the cell. In each case the specificity is observed in some functional uniqueness and is attributable to some structural individuality. Among the classes of substances other than proteins possessing specificity are the polysaccharides and nucleic acids. A useful way of demonstrating such specificity is through an extraordinary capacity of animals. If a foreign protein or polysaccharide or nucleic acid somehow gets into the body of a vertebrate, the animal's circulatory system manufactures *antibodies* (protein in nature) capable of binding firmly with the foreign, introduced substance, called an *antigen*. Antibodies too show a remarkable specificity, for they will bind—and often, in so doing, inactivate—only the specific antigen that elicited their formation. Thus, on inoculating purified enzyme molecules derived from *E. coli* into a rabbit, antibodies accumulate in the rabbit's blood and can be harvested by collecting the blood serum (so-called antiserum); this serum thereafter exhibits the property of binding and inactivating the particular *E. coli* enzyme used to invite antibody production in the rabbit.

5. *The least common denominator of specificity.*

Proteins, nucleic acids, and polysaccharides—all characterized by specificity—have this in common: they are large molecules made by connecting together simpler compounds in long chains. Polysaccharides are polymers composed of monosaccharides (sugars such as glucose, galactose, fructose, and conjugated sugars such as glucosamine). Proteins are polymers of amino acids, and nucleic acids are polymers of nucleotides. The constituent building-blocks of each class of macromolecular substance are relatively few in number, there being about twenty different amino acids, of which proteins may be composed, and several nucleotides, of which nucleic acids may be composed. (There are actually two kinds of nucleic acids, ribo- and deoxyribonucleic acids, about which more will be said later.) Thus, a variety of proteins can be constructed by varying the kinds and sequences of the amino acids utilized. Similarly, with four common nucleotides to choose from and a molecule possessing a million nucleotides to be constructed, an astronomically wide variety of deoxyribonucleic acids can be built. Biological specificity seems to be based on variations on a common theme, on variant arrangements of a few fundamental repeating units, or monomers, in a polymeric structure.

Mutation and Adaptation in Microorganisms

However potentially useful the microorganisms may seem, the legitimacy of using them in genetic research depends on the demonstration of an organized array of genes in these lowly organisms. Prior to 1940, some biologists doubted that microorganisms, especially the bacteria, possessed a mechanism of heredity similar to that of the higher plants and animals. ("Higher" and "lower" here refer, respectively, to more or less complex, more or less evolved forms of life.) The reason for doubt was the small size and relatively undifferentiated condition of the bacterial cell. The bacterium was so small, it was argued, that there was no effective separation of the environment from the genetic apparatus of the cell. Environmental changes impinged almost directly on the materials of which the bacterium was composed, and consequently, the bacterial phenotype was the result exclusively of environmental manipulation.

Such a view would, of course, mean that the bacterium was an extremely plastic and flexible individual, conforming only to the dictates of the external environment. Support for this view, however, was based largely on a misinterpretation of observations. It was known, for example, that if one exposed a culture of bacteria to some virus, many of the exposed bacteria might be killed by viral infection, but a few rare individuals survived. Moreover, from these rare survivors there descended a strain of *genetically* resistant individuals. Similar results were observed if one exposed a bacterial population to a drug or antibiotic, such as penicillin, that it had not encountered before—or if one inoculated the population into a medium in which the only source of energy was a compound that had not been utilized before. Usually, most of the individuals in the population died; the rare survivors were demonstrably different in their genetic properties, because most of the progeny to which they gave rise were able to withstand the drug or antibiotic, or were able to utilize the new energy source. If the environmental change (addition of virus or drug or antibiotic, or substitution of energy source) brought about the change in character in the rare survivors, it was causing an hereditary alteration, since the alteration was passed on to the progeny of the survivors. This sort of adaptation to environmental exigencies was exactly as Lamarck had suggested might account for the evolution of adapted species of higher plants and animals. Oddly enough, the Lamarckian theory of evolution had already been discarded for higher organisms, since environmental modifications of animals and plants were usually not inherited, and since gene mutations arose in a random way, exhibiting no necessary adaptive correspondence to the environment in which the mutations occurred.

In the foregoing description of bacterial adaptation, a distinction was made between the individual bacterium and the population or culture of which it was a part. This distinction, unfortunately, was not always made by bacteriologists in the past. Failure to make the distinction was responsible for the early misinterpretation of the phenomenon. After all, another way in which the environment could have acted in the cases already described was by selection (à la Darwin) of rare individuals which had already arisen in the population as a result of random mutation *prior* to the onset of the environmental change. Happily, ways have been developed to determine whether Lamarckian or Darwinian processes account for the adaptation of populations. One way we owe to S. E. Luria and M. Delbrück, who pointed out that the two models of adaptation make quite different statistical predictions. Imagine a number of tubes containing identical media and treated in a similar manner, each tube being inoculated with only a few cells of the same bacterial species. After the population has grown in size, the number of bacteria in each tube capable of withstanding a particular environmental change is expected to be quite similar according to the Lamarckian model, but is expected to be quite different according to the Darwinian view. According to the Lamarckian interpretation, every bacterium has the same small chance of adapting itself to the environmental stress, and therefore the number of adapted variants should only be a function of the total number of bacteria in the culture. Since the total numbers of bacteria in the parallel cultures are the same, the numbers of adaptable individuals in these cultures should be the same. The Darwinian view—really a post-Darwinian view which has adopted the notion of random genetic variations—asserts that, because of the randomness and rarity of mutations, a specific kind of mutational event may occur early or late during the growth of a given population. If it occurs early, there will be many individuals in the culture with the heritable adaptive trait; if it occurs late, there will be few such individuals in the culture. Thus, to discriminate between the two models, it simply requires determining how many bacteria in each parallel culture are capable of withstanding a certain environmental change. When such a test is done—and it has been carried out in numerous cases of bacterial adaptation to drug resistance, to virus resistance, and to energy source utilization—the Lamarckian model fails to be confirmed, whereas the Darwinian model is upheld.

Statistical discriminations, however, are often held in ill repute, even by scientists, for the strange opinion is maintained in some quarters that "you can prove anything with statistics." (How and why this opinion came about is not the subject of this book.) Final rejection of the Lamarckian interpretation of bacterial adaptation was, therefore, held in abeyance until Joshua and Esther Lederberg developed a technique for demonstrating directly the occurrence of bacterial mutations in the absence of environmental conditions in which the mutations have a selective advantage. The Luria-Delbrück type of analysis required the investigator eventually to expose populations to conditions of environmental stress, and the mutants are selected under such conditions. The Lederbergs devised a procedure in which the mutants could be selected indirectly. The procedure is simple, and it is outlined in Text Fig. 9. In brief, the procedure consists in spreading a bacterial population over the surface of a nonselective agar medium. After some growth has occurred on this surface, a disc containing a velvet face is pressed gently onto the surface; it is then removed and pressed onto the surface of another agar medium. While making the transfer, the orientation of the disc is maintained so that the "north pole" of one dish corresponds to the north

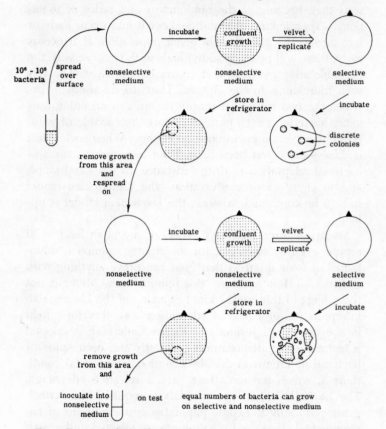

TEXT FIG. 9. The Lederbergs' experiment of indirect selection of bacterial mutants. The triangle (▲) at the top of a dish indicates a "north pole" reference point which is arbitrarily assigned to the "master" plate containing nonselective medium and which consequently fixes the "north pole" position of the corresponding "replica" plate containing selective medium. For details of the procedure by which a transfer from the "master" to the "replica" plate is made by means of a velvet-faced disc, see the text.

pole of the other. The velvet-faced disc transfers, in this way, a sample of the original growth which is attached to the firm fibers projecting perpendicularly from the velvet. By maintaining the orientation of the disc, one knows the general vicinity from which any portion of the sample has been transferred. The dish to which the sample is transferred contains a selective medium, that is, it will permit the growth only of adapted individuals capable of growing in the presence of a certain virus, a certain antibiotic, or a certain carbon source. If bacterial growth appears on any region of the dish containing selective medium, one may return to the original dish and remove growth from the region corresponding to that in which growth is observed in the selective dish. This removed growth—containing, on the random mutation hypothesis, the genetically adapted sisters of the individuals which grew on selective medium—is spread over a fresh dish of nonselective medium, and the test process is repeated. In a few such steps, one does in fact obtain, growing on nonselective medium, a bacterial population consisting predominantly of adapted mutants—although the mutants themselves never directly experienced the environmental stress to which they are adapted.

The Lederbergs' experiment of indirect selection of mutants has been repeated in so many different instances that there is no doubt any longer about the general validity of the random origin of heritable variations in bacteria—or for that matter in any other forms of microbial life. At least in this respect, microorganisms are no different from higher organisms. The question now arises whether the mutations occur in discrete units arranged in linear arrays.

The Mode of Genetic Recombination in Higher Organisms

The discreteness of genes is demonstrated by the separability of genes affecting different functions. This separability is generally achieved by the process of genetic recombination. It will be helpful to review some features of recombination in higher organisms before considering similar phenomena occurring in microorganisms.

Genetic recombination in the higher animals and plants occurs during a particular period of the life cycle. Text Fig. 10 summarizes the salient features. In the adult male and female of the species, gametes are produced within the sex organs. In animals, the male gametes are sperm and are produced in the testes; the female gametes are eggs and are

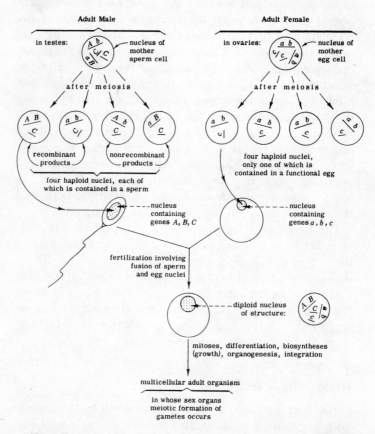

Text Fig. 10. Genetic recombination in the life cycle of higher organisms. Example: a sexually reproducing animal.

produced in the ovaries. The sperm are small and specialized for motility; the eggs are large and passive, specialized for storage of nutrients in the cytoplasm. After contact of the egg by a sperm, fertilization may consist in no more than the "infection," if you will, of the egg cell by a haploid nucleus from the sperm. The haploid sperm and egg nuclei meet and fuse to give rise to the single diploid nucleus of the fertilized egg, or zygote. The zygote undergoes mitotic divisions; it eventually grows in size as biosynthetic processes increase within the cells arising from mitosis; the cells differentiate chemically and morphologically; differentiated cells form specifically organized aggregates as tissues and organs; the functioning of the organs is coordinated so that an integrated organism is the normal outcome at any stage of development. A multicellular adult organism is the result of development, and in its sex organs a new crop of gametes are produced to insure a new turn of the life cycle.

In this life cycle, genetic recombination occurs in two ways, and each way at a different time. Genes located on nonhomologous chromosomes get mixed when the chromosomes contributed by different parents get mixed in fertilization. In Text Fig. 10, the genes A and C get *mixed into the same nucleus* with their alleles a and c as a consequence of fertilization. On the other hand, genes located on homologous chromosomes may get *mixed into the same chromosome* as a result of exchanges during meiosis. In Text Fig. 10, the male gamete bearing genes A and B was the result of a recombination between homologous chromosomes containing Ab and aB, respectively. The latter type of recombination has already been discussed, and since it results from physical exchanges *within* chromosomes, it may be referred to as *intrachromosomal recombination*. The former type of recombination is due to the shuffling of chromosomes inherent in meiotic reduction and the restoration of diploidy through fertilization. It may be referred to as *interchromosomal recombination*.

By whichever way recombination occurs, it is of tremendous significance in evolution. In diploid organisms, recessive alleles may be masked by their dominant counterparts, and in heterozygotes, deleterious recessive alleles may be sheltered from the selective action of the environment. But, as has already been mentioned, whether or not a gene allele is deleterious depends in part on the environment and in part on the residual portion of the genotype. Through genetic recombination, initially deleterious alleles, leading a protected existence in heterozygotes, may come to be part of new complexes of genes. Certain of these gene combinations may be extremely valuable for the species as a whole to possess, for they may confer adaptive (far from deleterious) properties in the same or possibly a new environment. The phenomena of dominance, diploidy, and genetic recombination play, therefore, important roles in the evolution of the sexually reproducing higher organisms.

The Mode of Genetic Recombination in Molds

In molds, similar phenomena play equally important roles. There are two distinct differences in the nature of the mold's life cycle. On the one hand, the portion of the life cycle in which the mold is haploid is considerably greater than that of the higher organisms. Indeed, shortly after fertilization, when the diploid condition is restored, meiosis ensues to give rise to haploid nuclei, which is the condition of most of the nuclei of the mold during the course of its growth. On the other hand, reproduction is divorced from recombination, so that increase in the number of mold organisms can occur without necessitating gamete production, fertilization, or recombination. These features of the mold's life cycle are shown in Text Fig. 11.

Although not shown in the figure, many nuclei share a common cytoplasm in the mold mycelium. Occasionally the hyphae of different mold organisms, differing in genotype, may meet and fuse so as to produce a mixed mycelium. This mycelium is said to be a *heterokaryon*, because nuclei containing different genic contents share a common cytoplasm. Heterokaryosis is very important, because it permits the

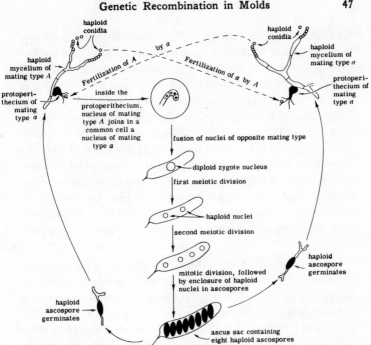

TEXT FIG. 11. Genetic recombination in the life cycle of a mold. Example: *Neurospora crassa*. The mold *Neurospora crassa* grows by elongation of its haploid mycelium and multiplies asexually by budding off haploid conidial spores from its aerial hyphae. The conidia are dispersed by air currents and germinate in suitable environments to give rise to new mycelial growths. Sexual reproduction is achieved when a conidium of one mating type lands on the filamentous extensions (trichogynes) of a fruiting body (protoperithecium) of opposite mating type. The sketches in the central region of this figure indicate the major ensuing events. A nucleus (darkened circle) of the fertilizing conidium comes to reside in a cell containing a nucleus (open circle) of protoperithicial origin. These two nuclei fuse to produce the diploid zygote nucleus. The nuclear fusion is followed by two meiotic divisions and then a mitotic division. The eight resulting haploid nuclei are enclosed in tough-walled ascospores, which are contained, in turn, in a thin sac, or ascus.

The ascospores eventually emerge from the ascus and germinate under appropriate conditions, such as a brief rise in temperature, to give rise to new mycelial growths. The events of fertilization and meiosis permit recombination of genes contributed by the parents of opposite mating type. From R. P. Wagner and H. K. Mitchell, "Genetics and Metabolism," 2nd ed. Wiley, New York, 1964.

same sheltering of initially deleterious alleles as does diploidy in higher organisms; a dominant allele in one nucleus may permit the survival of a deleterious recessive allele in another nucleus. In a mold such as *Neurospora* (shown in Text Fig. 11), genetic recombination is achieved whenever fusion occurs between hyphae differing in mating type. In such a case, the nuclei of the fusing hyphae fuse in turn to produce a diploid zygote nucleus. Meiosis follows shortly afterward, so that haploid nuclei with recombinant chromosomes result. Each of these haploid nuclei is contained in an ascospore possessing a tough envelope. The ascospores are widely dispersed in nature, and then each ascospore germinates under suitable conditions to give rise to a new mycelium.

In other molds, fusion between sexually differentiated hyphae never occurs to produce sexual ascospore products. In certain species of *Aspergillus* and *Penicillium*, however, a parasexual process replaces sexual reproduction. This process is based on the phenomenon of heterokaryosis common to many filamentous molds. In the heterokaryon, fusion of like or unlike nuclei may occur at a low frequency. This results in rare, diploid nuclei in a predominantly haploid, heterokaryotic mycelium. Although it has not been previously mentioned, the phenomenon of recombination is known to occur during mitosis as well. So-called somatic recombination, however, is rare. In *Aspergillus* or *Penicillium*, it can be observed to occur occasionally in the diploid nuclei produced by the fusion of unlike haploid nuclei. These rare recombinations may be detected when two other events transpire: the haploidization of diploid nuclei, which is itself an infrequently occurring process, and the normal segregation of haploid nuclei into asexual conidiospores (see Text Fig. 11). The characters determined by genes in originally separate nuclei may now come to be expressed by a single haploid nucleus. Thus, in certain *Aspergillus* and *Penicillium* species, the parasexual process serves to furnish the genetic recombinations that are so valuable in evolution.

Modes of Genetic Recombination in Bacteria: Transformation

The nuclei of molds are not much different in appearance from those of higher plants or animals. No such organelle is found within the tiny bacterial cell. By careful methods, however, it is possible to distinguish a bacterial organelle that very likely assumes the responsibilities of the nucleus of the more complex cell. Sometimes referred to as the "Robinow body" (in honor of the bacterial cytologist who stressed its significance) or "chromatinic structure" (because of the kind of material contained within it), it shall be referred to here as a *nucleoid*. The nucleoid is a discrete structure assuming somewhat different shapes in different bacteria. There are usually two or more nucleoids per cell in a given bacterial culture, depending on the prevailing physiological conditions. What arouses our interest in them are the way in which they are reproduced and their chemical constitution. During bacterial multiplication, the nucleoids grow, divide, and are distributed to daughter cells in a very regular manner. Indeed, the multiplication of the nucleoids is synchronized with that of cell division, so that every daughter gets at least one nucleoid. The nucleoids are also observed to contain a substance characteristically found in the chromosomes of higher organisms. This substance is deoxyribonucleic acid, or DNA (a special type of nucleic acid, about which more will be said later). The presence of DNA can be detected by dyes that specifically stain DNA and by its vulnerability to an enzyme (DNase) that depolymerizes DNA. Elegant confirmation that the nucleoid is the residence of the genetic material of the bacterium was made by Evelyn Witkin, who showed that the transmission of a radiation-induced mutation to the progeny of the irradiated bacterium could be predicted by the segregation of nucleoids during division of a multinucleate bacterial population.

Shortly before it was discovered that bacterial nucleoids are composed principally of DNA, an important property of DNA had already been demonstrated. In 1944, O. T.

Avery and two of his colleagues at the Rockefeller Institute, M. McCarty and C. M. MacLeod, showed that DNA could convey genetic information from one bacterium to another. Avery and his associates had been studying for a decade the chemical nature of the substance responsible for an extraordinary phenomenon first reported by the English bacteriologist, F. Griffith, in 1927. Griffith had observed that a heat-killed vaccine of virulent pneumococci (the bacteria causing pneumonia) could convert an avirulent pneumococcal mutant into a disease-producer when a mixture of the vaccine and avirulent bacteria was inoculated into mice. Later investigators showed that the transformation could be carried out in a test tube and that the vaccine of killed, virulent organisms could be replaced by a chemical extract of these organisms. It was clear, moreover, that the transformation was genetic, in the sense that the transformed bacteria reproduced to yield progeny that continued to possess the virulent character. The transformation was not only heritable, it was also specific, for the particular type of disease produced by the transformed bacteria was exactly like that of the bacteria from which the chemical extract was obtained. Something in the extract was capable of conveying genetic information, and Avery's group proceeded to determine what it was.

Avery, MacLeod, and McCarty provided strong evidence that DNA was that substance. They showed that the transforming activity of the extract was unaffected by enzymes that depolymerize proteins, by chemical agents that denature proteins, by enzymes that attack ribonucleic acid (the other principal type of nucleic acid found in cells, about which more will be said later), or by antibodies that bind pneumococcal proteins and polysaccharides. On the contrary, an enzyme that rapidly and irreversibly destroyed the transforming activity was DNase. A purified fraction of the extract that still possessed transforming activity contained hydrogen, carbon, nitrogen, and phosphorus atoms in almost exactly the same proportions as they are found in DNA extracted from animal tissues. Tests for protein in the purified fraction were negative.

The conclusion by Avery's group that DNA is the transforming agent was all the more praiseworthy, because it was announced at a time when the function of DNA in cells was still unknown. There is, of course, a good deal of circumstantial evidence, some of it known then and some learned later, that DNA is an important substance. DNA is found almost exclusively in the chromosomes of higher organisms and in the nucleoids of bacteria. The quantity of DNA in a given cell is directly related to the number of chromosome sets. Thus, diploid cells contain twice as much DNA as haploid cells of the same species, and the amount of DNA is doubled before a cell undergoes mitosis. The same regularity in molecular replication associated with cellular reproduction is not observed for any other class of molecules. Yet the novelty of assigning genetic specificity to DNA required further experimental verification. This did not take long in coming. Whatever caused a structural denaturation in the molecules of DNA, which were known to be in purified transforming preparations, caused a loss of transforming activity; indeed, transforming activity was quantitatively related to the native integrity of the DNA molecule. Therefore, it was clear that DNA was essential for the genetic transformation of bacteria. Was it sufficient? Rollin Hotchkiss in particular made strenuous efforts to free transforming preparations of detectable traces of substances other than DNA; such preparations were still active in transformation. The sufficiency of DNA as a transforming agent will be most convincingly demonstrated when DNA with transforming activity is synthesized *in vitro*. How this may be done will be discussed in a subsequent chapter, where the structure and synthesis of DNA will be treated.

The use of isotopes has provided a powerful biochemical technique for tracing the route of substances through various processes of the cell. This technique has been applied to follow the DNA molecule as it brings about genetic transformation. By growing bacteria in a medium containing phosphate, the phosphorus atoms of which are in the isotopic form of P^{32}, biological synthesis is obliged to incorporate P^{32} into the phosphorus-containing compounds. The P^{32} label is readily detectable because it is radioactive, emitting beta particles which can be monitored by radioactivity counting devices. DNA contains phosphorus, and therefore one can obtain a preparation of P^{32}-labeled transforming DNA. During transformation, the P^{32} label enters the host bacterium and usually remains associated with an intact DNA molecule. Indeed, the number of host bacteria that are transformed is directly proportional to the number of P^{32}-labeled, intact DNA molecules bound inside the bacteria. This finding tells us that it is sufficient for one molecule of DNA to enter a cell to trigger events leading to the cell's transformation.

Since transformation was discovered in pneumococcus by Griffith, numerous other species of bacteria have been found to be transformable by means of DNA. The transformable species are not all closely related to each other, since the bacteriologist finds so many differences between them as to suggest that they belong to groups which have diverged in the course of evolution. One important aspect of transformation is that the DNA of one species will only transform bacteria of the same or of a very closely related species. The inability of DNA to transform bacteria of another species appears to be due not to a failure to penetrate the host bacteria, but to a failure to effect transformation once inside. In any event, transformation is not restricted to a single species of bacterium. Moreover, transformation appears to occur in nature. At least, living cultures of bacteria liberate DNA as they grow, and if such DNA comes from a mutant, it may transform other, nonmutant bacteria in the same population. Therefore, there is reason to believe that transformation may be a natural mode of genetic recombination in bacteria. What may be a critical factor in the natural occurrence of transformation is the requirement that bacteria must be physiologically competent to be transformed. This physiological state of competence is transient in growing bacterial cultures (although it literally can be "frozen" by placing competent cells into a "deep freeze"), and, to be developed, depends upon several as yet poorly understood conditions. There are at least two components of competence, one of which affects the ability of the transforming DNA molecule to penetrate the host, and the other of which affects the ability of the molecule to complete transformation once inside.

Not only does transformation occur in a wide variety of bacteria, it is capable of affecting every genetic character of the bacterium. Nearly any character that is subject to mutation may also be transformed by the appropriate DNA. Thus, penicillin-sensitive bacteria may be made genetically penicillin-resistant upon exposure to DNA from penicillin-resistant bacteria. In a similar way, nonutilizers of the sugar maltose can be transformed into utilizers, or nonsynthesizers of the amino acid tryptophan into synthesizers of tryptophan, and so on. If one transforms a bacterial culture with DNA extracted from a strain that is mutant in two or more characters, the result is a mixture of transformed bacteria. Most transformants acquire only one of the mutant determinants from the so-called DNA donor strain. Some determinants are transferred independently of each other, others are transferred in a linked fashion. These findings mean that a molecule of DNA bears more than one piece of genetic information, but the chance is not great that a transformed bacterium will acquire all of the genetic information on the infecting DNA molecule. The findings do not necessarily imply that there is more than one species of DNA molecule in the intact bacterium, or that determinants transferred independently of each other are borne on different species of DNA molecules, for if recombination between DNA molecules can separate genetically linked determinants, then it might separate some determinants so often that they would be effectively integrated in an independent fashion.

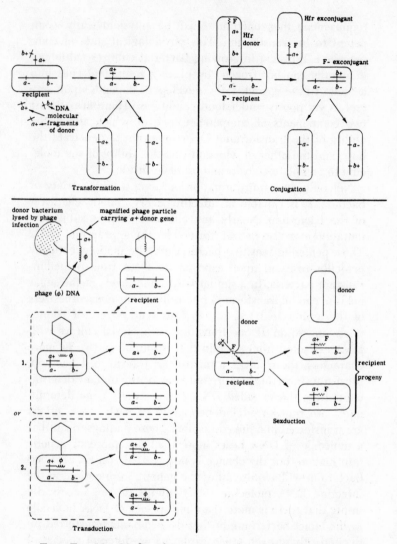

TEXT FIG. 12. Modes of genetic recombination in bacteria.

Transformation: DNA molecules or molecular fragments released by a donor strain of bacterium, not shown in the diagram, make contact with and penetrate a competent recipient. In reproducing, the recipient gives rise to bacteria in whose chromosomes a donor gene $(a+)$

What happens once the infecting DNA molecule is inside a host bacterium? Evidence is just beginning to be evinced on this question. First of all, it should be made clear that transformations are reversible. Thus, a bacterium that is made streptomycin-resistant, by acquiring DNA from a streptomycin-resistant mutant, may be retransformed into a streptomycin-sensitive bacterium by exposing it to DNA

---

has replaced its homologue (a—) originally in the recipient. It is not certain whether all of the recipient's progeny contain the donor gene or, as shown in the diagram, only half (or less) do.

Conjugation: An Hfr donor bacterium transfers its chromosome to an F- recipient. The transfer is usually incomplete. Donor genes ($b+$) that have been transferred are found to be recombined with recipient genes (a—) in the chromosomes of progeny descending from the F- exconjugant.

Transduction: A bacteriophage released by a lysing (donor) bacterium may carry, in addition to its own specific DNA (ϕ), a gene ($a+$) from the donor chromosome. Infection of a recipient bacterium by such a bacteriophage particle may result in one of the following two situations, depending on the particular bacterium-bacteriophage system involved: (1) In *generalized* transduction, the donor gene is stably integrated into the chromosomes of (at least some) recipient progeny. Integration of the bacteriophage DNA need not accompany integration of the donor gene. (2) In *specialized* transduction, the transducing bacteriophage is defective. Although not indicated in the diagram, part of its own genetic material is replaced by the donor gene it carries. Infection in this case results in a partially diploid bacterium in which the transduced donor gene ($a+$) is carried along with the homologue (a—) originally in the recipient. This partially diploid condition is unstable, and once in a thousand generations, the extra chromosomal piece is discarded leaving the bacterium stably a—, as the original recipient had been, or stably $a+$.

Sexduction: Occasionally during conjugation, the fertility factor (F) responsible for making a cell a donor carries with it a gene from the donor bacterium into the recipient. A partially diploid condition is set up, similar to that which occurs in specialized transduction.

For the sake of simplicity, the bacteria are shown as possessing a single chromosome. In actuality, there may be two or more identical nucleoids (chromosomes) per cell. The bacterial chromosome, moreover, may occur in the form of a closed loop, and not as a line as indicated.

from a streptomycin-sensitive donor. The facility of reversing transformations by using the appropriate DNA means that bacteria are probably haploid (and there is considerable supplementary evidence on this point), and that transformation consists in the replacement of an endogenous gene by a homologous factor, or allele, arriving exogenously. How does this replacement occur? The available evidence suggests that a physical exchange takes place between the endogenous and exogenous DNA, that whatever is left of the exogenous material is eliminated once part of it is inserted into the endogenous DNA. How we have arrived at this knowledge will be one of the subjects of Chapter IV, in which we will examine how recombination between DNA molecules takes place and the extent to which molecular recombination can account for chromosomal recombination in higher organisms. A diagrammatic summary of the principal events in transformation is furnished in Text Fig. 12.

There are other interesting questions that we must postpone. How does the integrated piece of donor DNA influence the production of a new character in the host bacterium? What are the barriers to the flow of DNA between species? For the present, we must continue our exploration of modes of genetic recombination in bacteria.

Modes of Genetic Recombination in Bacteria: Lysogeny and Lysogenic Conversion; Bacteriophage Recombination

Genetic transfer between bacteria may also be mediated by viruses. Until the rise of molecular genetics during the last two decades, such a notion would have been difficult to imagine. For viruses are usually associated with production of disease, and not until recently have biologists learned that viruses may infect their hosts without doing any damage. Viruses are small but well-organized entities. They are small enough to pass through the pores of filters which block the passage of bacteria, but they can be photographed by means of the electron microscope. Their shapes are quite characteristic, different kinds of viruses exhibiting specific geometric patterns in their external morphology (see Plate 4). Some viruses are as small as 15 mμ in diameter. Some viruses infect plants, and usually only certain ones (the tobacco mosaic virus and the tomato bushy stunt virus, for example); some viruses infect animals, and usually only certain cells in certain species (the poliomyelitis virus which invades the motor cells in the spinal cord of man, for example); still other viruses infect bacteria, and are called bacteriophages (bacteria-eaters; the T2 or T4 bacteriophage that infects *E. coli*, for example). The viruses also vary a good deal in their chemical organization. Among the animal viruses are many that are quite large and chemically complex. All viruses contain at least protein and nucleic acid, and the nucleic acid is usually either of the RNA or the DNA type.

Alfred Hershey and Martha Chase were the first to show that viral invasion of a cell involves primarily the viral nucleic acid. They used bacteriophage which contains only protein and DNA, and grew the viruses on bacterial hosts in a medium containing radioactive sulfur (S^{35}) and phosphorus (P^{32}). As a result, the viral proteins, which contain sulfur, but not phosphorus, were labeled with S^{35}, and the viral DNA, which contains phosphorus, but not sulfur, was labeled with P^{32}. Hershey and Chase then allowed unlabeled bacteria to make contact with the labeled bacteriophage, and shortly after contact, detached whatever remained of the virus from the bacterial walls by shaking the bacteriophage-bacterial complexes in a Waring blendor. The brief contact between bacteriophage and bacterium is essential, for unless it occurs, no infection ensues. Contact results in attachment of the virus to the outer wall of the bacterium, in which position much of the virus remains. The Waring blendor treatment revealed that it is mostly viral protein that remains outside the bacteria, for the treatment detaches protein, but allows practically all of the viral DNA to enter.

This was shown by the fact that the S^{35} label was recoverable in the culture medium, but the P^{32} label was inside the bacteria. Once inside, the viral DNA carried out the usual events of viral infection. Subsequent experiments by other virologists demonstrated that, in the case of invasion of animal cells by poliomyelitis virus or invasion of tobacco cells by mosaic virus, the nucleic acid component of the virus alone enters the host cells. These latter cases are especially interesting, because the nucleic acid of the poliomyelitis and tobacco mosaic viruses is of the RNA type. The experiments with labeled viruses confirm, therefore, that nucleic acids are carriers of genetic information, and they establish RNA, as well as DNA, in the class of molecules bearing genetic specificity. For those who might inquire what kind of genetic information is introduced with the infecting viral nucleic acid, the answer resides in the fact that viral infection makes possible the production of a great many (100 or more) virus particles of the kind that infected the hosts. Therefore, viral nucleic acid contains the information necessary to specify the structures of the protein and nucleic acid components of virus, and the information necessary to put these components together in the specifically organized way characteristic of extracellular, so-called *mature* virus.

While production of additional virus particles is *potentiated* by the introduction of bacteriophage DNA, such an outcome does not always result. Bacteriophages like T2 are said to be virulent, because absorption by its host of a single T2 particle generally leads to dissolution of the bacterium, accompanied by liberation of many more T2 particles. Other bacteriophages like λ are said to be temperate, because the chances are favorable that infection will not lead to bacterial death, but rather to a symbiotic condition in which bacterium and bacteriophage remain associated in what may be regarded as a mutually satisfactory condition. Infection of *E. coli* by DNA from bacteriophage λ does result, in a certain percentage of the cases, in virus production and cell death. But in a high percentage of cases, the exact extent of which is influenced by environmental conditions, the infected bacterium continues to grow and multiply. However, there are two marked changes in such a bacterium. First of all, the bacterium gains the ability to reproduce the infecting DNA, as evidenced by the fact that the infected bacterium and its asexual descendants can be induced to manufacture mature bacteriophage particles. Induction of bacteriophage reproduction can be achieved by irradiating the bacteria with ultraviolet light or by treating the bacteria with certain chemical agents. Induction results in bacterial lysis and liberation of a crop of mature λ bacteriophage. A bacterium thus demonstrated to contain the genetic information of a virus is said to be *lysogenic* because it can be induced to manufacture virus particles. Further evidence that the lysogenic bacterium carries the bacteriophage DNA is the fact that an occasional descendant (about one in a hundred thousand) of the lysogenic bacterium does produce the virus spontaneously. The second significant change in the lysogenized bacterium is the immunity it acquires. As a result of the continued presence of λ DNA, the lysogenic bacterium is immune to any subsequent infection by λ or bacteriophages related to λ. This immunity appears to result from the manufacture, under the direction of λ DNA, of an immunity substance which represses the vegetative reproduction of superinfecting λ DNA, as well as of the λ DNA already in the bacterium. Thus, bacteriophage DNA also carries the genetic information for conferring immunity upon its host. By certain treatments, the lysogenized bacterium can be "cured" of the bacteriophage DNA it is carrying. When it is cured, however, it loses the ability to manufacture mature virus, and it also loses immunity to infection by specific bacteriophages.

A lysogenic bacterium may be said to have acquired certain hereditary properties that it did not possess prior to infection. These properties are dependent upon the continued presence of the bacteriophage DNA. Although the properties that have just been discussed are related to bacteriophage reproduction, other properties may be acquired that have no obvious connection to bacteriophage structure or function. For example, certain *Salmonella* strains (intestinal bacteria related to *E. coli*) produce specific antigens in their cell walls only when they are lysogenized by a certain bacteriophage. Another interesting example is that of the diphtheria bacillus, which is harmful primarily when it secretes a highly poisonous substance (an exotoxin). This exotoxin is eventually carried about in the blood of a person infected with diphtheria bacilli, and it is responsible for poisoning the respiratory processes and causing death. Production of the exotoxin can be shown, however, to take place only in diphtheria bacilli lysogenic for a certain bacteriophage. Bacilli that are not lysogenic for this phage do not manufacture the exotoxin and are not pathogenic. *Lysogenic conversion* is the term applied to hereditary changes in bacterial characters due to the maintenance of a lysogenic condition.

Lysogeny is a curious state in which the synthesis of bacteriophage DNA is integrated with bacterial reproduction. Genetic analysis, by a process to be described in the next section, has shown that integration of bacteriophage DNA is associated with the attachment of bacteriophage DNA to bacterial DNA. While demonstration of this fact must be deferred, it is clear that an operational distinction can be made between an integrated state of bacteriophage DNA and a state in which synthesis of bacteriophage DNA is unregulated. This latter, autonomous state is the one in which bacteriophage DNA is rapidly synthesized in the host bacterium, just prior to its incorporation into mature virus particles. It is the state associated with lysis of the host and typical of virulent bacteriophages. For this reason, one speaks of the *lytic* versus the *lysogenic* types of bacteriophage reproduction. The major features distinguishing the lytic from the lysogenic infection are schematically summarized in Text Fig. 13. Moreover, since the lysogenic infection is characterized by the regulated synthesis of bacteriophage DNA in the host bacterium, and not by the production of mature bacteriophage particles (consisting of

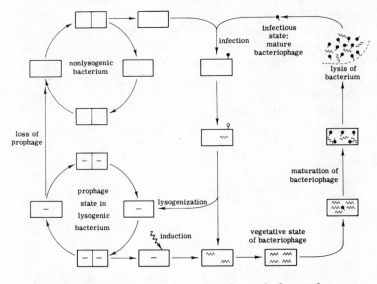

TEXT FIG. 13.   Lytic versus lysogenic infection by bacterial viruses. When the DNA of a temperate bacteriophage penetrates a bacterial host, two alternative situations are possible: (1) The bacteriophage DNA may multiply vegetatively, resulting, eventually, in maturation of the virus particles and lysis of the host. In mature bacteriophage, the DNA is enclosed within a protein coat; in this form it is infectious. This *lytic* type of infection is shown on the right hand side of the diagram. (2) The bacteriophage DNA may multiply in synchrony with bacterial DNA. In this integrated state, the bacteriophage is referred to as prophage. The host is lysogenic, for under appropriate conditions, the prophage may be induced to enter the vegetative state and cause a typical lytic infection. The lysogenic type of infection is shown in the lower left hand side of the diagram. Under certain conditions, the prophage may be lost, making the host nonlysogenic, as shown in the upper left hand side of the diagram. In contradistinction to the nonlysogenic bacterium, the lysogenized bacterium is ordinarily immune to secondary infection by a mature bacteriophage of the same species. [The diagram is based on one by A. Lwoff, *Bacteriol. Revs.* 17, 269-337 (1953).]

DNA enclosed in a highly organized way within protein coats), one should speak of the bacteriophage being in a *prophage* state in the lysogenic bacterium. The replication of prophage DNA is clearly different from that of *vegetative* phage DNA, which is multiplying in an autonomous way within the host and also causing the production of phage proteins within which it will become enclosed. One of the outstanding problems of molecular genetics today is to discover the factors *controlling* the replication of bacteriophage DNA. These factors may elucidate the mechanism controlling DNA replication in cells in general.

When bacteriophage DNA is multiplying vegetatively during a lytic infection, or subsequent to induction by ultraviolet light, the DNA replicas are observed to recombine with each other. This may be readily demonstrated in the following way. Bacteriophages are capable of mutation; the mutations may be expressed as changes in the kinds of bacterial hosts that may be successfully infected by the phages. For example, bacteriophage T4 rII is a mutant form of T4 which can produce lytic infections in strain B of *E. coli*, but not in the K12 strain of *E. coli* carrying λ prophage, although the wild-type T4 phage can lytically infect both strains. Other mutations in T4 bacteriophage may occur so as to alter the rate at which the bacterial host is lysed. If one infects strain B bacteria *simultaneously* with a mutant of each type, mature phage particles are produced. On analysis, these virus particles prove to be not only of the original mutant types, but also genetic recombinants. The recombinants may be either nonmutated (i.e., wild type), with respect to both host specificity and speed of lysis, or doubly mutated. Evidently vegetative DNA molecules, in the course of their multiplication, interact with each other so as to produce recombinant forms. At this stage of our discussion, we may rightfully wonder whether recombination between vegetative bacteriophage DNA particles is equivalent to the genetic recombination that occurs between host and donor molecules in transformation.

Modes of Genetic Recombination in Bacteria: Conjugation

The work of Avery's group on transformation was published in 1944. The genetics of bacteriophage began to be studied vigorously in the 1940's, after Max Delbrück developed techniques for the study of bacteriophage infection in single bacteria and demonstrated the phenomenon of phage recombination. Shortly afterwards, in 1946, another important discovery was made concerning recombination occurring within bacteria. This was the discovery by Lederberg and Tatum of bacterial conjugation. A great deal of work has been done to elucidate the mechanism of this complex phenomenon, and rather than trace the somewhat tortuous path by which our present knowledge has been gained, it will be more profitable and economical to present a synthesis of available facts and interpretations. The currently accepted picture of the events underlying bacterial conjugation is owed largely to the investigations of Joshua Lederberg in the United States, William Hayes in England, and François Jacob and Elie Wollman in France.

First observed in the K12 strain of *Escherichia coli*, conjugation has subsequently been demonstrated to occur in other species of bacteria, including closely related (*Salmonella* and *Shigella*) and remotely related (*Pseudomonas*) species. Initially, the phenomenon is detected on mixing two populations of the same species, but differing from each other in two or more hereditary characters. The two populations are usually obtained by accumulation of independent mutations in an originally wild-type population. Thus, mutant population 1 may be a— b— x+ y+ and mutant population 2 may be a+ b+ x— y—, where a, b, x, and y represent different bacterial characters (such as the ability to utilize lactose as a carbon source or the ability to grow and reproduce in the presence of streptomycin) and + and — represent alternative conditions of the character (such as ability vs. inability). After mixing the two populations, samples of the mixture are inoculated into a solid agar medium which allows growth of only certain individuals. The constituents of the medium can be arranged so that, for example, only a+ b+ x+ y+ bacteria can multiply to produce visible colonies. On inoculating 10^6 bacteria from mutant population 1 or 2 into such a selective medium, no colonies are formed. On inoculating a million bacteria from the mixture of mutant populations 1 and 2, many colonies are observed to form on the selective medium. These colonies, when isolated and tested, are found to contain a+ b+ x+ y+ bacteria, or, in other words, bacteria which have recombined the a+ and b+ genetic determinants of mutant population 1 with the x+ and y+ genetic determinants of mutant population 2.

Indeed, if the two mutant populations of *E. coli* K12 differ in respect to many genetic characters, the recombination of all the characters can be found in a relatively high proportion of the recombinant bacteria. This phenomenon is obviously different from transformation, in which usually only a single genetic character is changed per transformed cell. Moreover, the enzyme DNase, which depolymerizes DNA and inactivates a transforming DNA preparation, cannot prevent the multifactorial recombination that occurs between *E. coli* K12 cells. To determine whether a virus passes from bacterial cell to cell, carrying with it genetic determinants of its previous host and, in this way, mediating the observed recombinations, the two recombining populations may be inoculated into separate arms of a U-shaped tube in the neck of which is a filter. The filter prevents bacteria from passing, but allows chemical molecules and virus particles to pass freely. The nonbacterial contents of the two arms of the tube may be constantly mixed by alternating pressure on the mouths of the arms. If one keeps the mutant populations separated in this manner, although allowing them to share the same culture medium, including any bacteriophage particles liberated into the medium, the phenomenon of recombination in *E. coli* K12 is prevented. This experiment demonstrates that physical contact between the bacteria is essential for this mode of recombination. Electron microscopy has revealed that the recombining bacteria do indeed form intimate couples, and, in the cellular region where the couple is connected, a "protoplasmic bridge" forms between one bacterium and its mate (see Plate 2). For this reason, this mode of recombination is called *conjugation*, and the recombining bacteria are referred to as *conjugants*.

With the further study of conjugation, it was learned that genetic material flows from one conjugant to the other. However, this transfer proceeds in only one direction. One of the conjugants is the donor, and the other is the recipient. This fact is readily revealed by observing conjugation with the light microscope and using conjugants that are visibly different in size and shape. Conjugation is rapid and apparently very efficient, since most of the morphologically different bacteria get together. After the couples form, individual couples are isolated into separate droplets by means of a device known as a micromanipulator. When a sufficient number of minutes has elapsed to allow genetic transfer, the conjugants are physically separated from each other, again by means of the micromanipulator. Each *exconjugant* is allowed to multiply and produce a *clone* of asexual descendants. Progeny bearing recombined characters of the two conjugating parents are found in only one of the two clones. Thus, only one of the parents, the recipient parent, gives rise to recombinant progeny; the other parent, the donor, gives rise exclusively to nonrecombinant progeny. (The donor survives conjugation and can reproduce because it is multinucleoid; probably only one nucleoid is transferred during conjugation.)

The donor bacterium differs from the recipient by possession of an agent, called a fertility factor or F+. The F+ factor is responsible for changes in the protein constituents of the cell membrane of the donor. The protein differences in the membranes of donor and recipient bacteria are believed to account for the coupling phenomenon that precedes actual genetic transfer. There are many F+ factors per donor cell, and a recipient (called F—) generally receives at least one such F+ factor during conjugation, regardless of how much other genetic material is transferred from the donor. The F+ agent behaves, therefore, like an infectious agent, and it can very rapidly convert an F— population into an F+ population with characteristic donor properties. By careful investigation, one finds that not all donor bacteria behave similarly during conjugation. Most donors transmit nothing more than F+ factors to the conjugating F— recipients. Rare mutant donors transmit very large groups of genes and, at the same time, transmit F+ with greatly reduced efficiency. These mutant donors that transmit their genes in big clusters are called "Hfr," because, when they are isolated, they can be used as donors that transfer genetic material at high frequency (Hfr) to F— recipient bacteria. Whereas with the usual F+ population the frequency of recombinants bearing a given donor gene is on the order of 10^{-5} conjugations, the frequency of such recombinants obtained when an Hfr donor is used may be as high as 10^{-1} couplings.

The Hfr mutants that are isolated from an F+ donor population are not all the same, although they have a great deal in common. Let us consider first of all what characterizes the Hfr bacteria as a group. If a particular Hfr strain is used to conjugate with a given F— strain, all of the known genetic determinants of the Hfr donor are observed to pass to the F— recipient. Moreover, the donor determinants are observed to pass in a regular, continuous sequence. If one interrupts conjugation by mechanically separating the conjugants or by selectively destroying the Hfr donors, one finds that the transfer of a given donor gene is prevented, *depending*, however, on the time after the initial mixing of the Hfr and F— bacteria when mating is interrupted. This time is characteristic of each gene, but varies from gene to gene. Thus, gene C may be transferred early and gene W relatively late, so that the transfer of C can be blocked only if mating is interrupted relatively early, but the transfer of W can be blocked even if mating is interrupted relatively late. A linear order or progression of genes is thus observed to pass from Hfr to F— bacteria. This order is reasonably interpreted as due to the passage of the structure that organizes the bacterial genes into a linear array. Although this organizing structure may be quite different in its physical and chemical properties from the chromosome of higher plants and animals, the term "chromosome" has been applied to this bacterial organelle as well. In any event, this experiment of interrupted mating shows that the bacterial genes are, in fact, physically linked, as we might have expected them to be on purely *a priori* grounds.

If mating is not interrupted, and conjugation is allowed to go on until the maximum yield of recombinants is recovered, one does not observe equal frequencies of recombination for all characters. On the contrary, every donor gene is found with a characteristic frequency among the total number of recombinants, but this frequency varies from gene to gene. Indeed, the *order of recombination frequencies* corresponds exactly to the *order of transfer frequencies* determined from the interrupted mating experiments. On these grounds, therefore, it is supposed that interruption of chromosomal transfer from Hfr donor to F— recipient is a *normal* feature of conjugation. The farther away a donor gene is from the chromosomal extremity which enters first, the less chance it will have of appearing in any recombinant. In this interpretation of conjugation, therefore, the F— exconjugants are heterogeneous; a great many have received the proximal (first-entering) portion of the donor chromosome, a few have received as much as a half of the donor chromosome, and very few have received an entire donor chromosome. Most of the F— exconjugants are, in this view, partially zygotic, and differ in the extent of donor chromosome received.

These properties characterize all Hfr donor strains. Hfr strains of independent origin do differ, however, in one important respect. While each strain exhibits a specific progression of genes transferred to recipient bacteria, the order varies from one strain to another. The only way in which the orders vary, however, is in the initial point of entry, O. The immediate neighbors of any gene are always the same, unless the gene occurs at the very beginning or end of the gene progression. Thus, for example, if the order for Hfr strain 1 is $O–C–E–W–A–Z–B–D–N–X$, the order for Hfr strain 2 may be $O–W–A–Z–B–D–N–X–C–E$, and the order for Hfr strain 3 may exhibit a reversed polarity $O–D–B–Z–$ tent if one supposes that the bacterial chromosome is a $A–W–E–C–X–N$. All of these facts can be rendered consistent if one supposes that the bacterial chromosome is a single continuous loop, and that, at conjugation, the loop breaks at some specific site. According to this interpretation, the location of this site, as well as the polarity with which the chromosome enters an F— bacterium, must be specifically determined by each Hfr strain. One further fact characterizes all Hfr gene orders, and it has not been mentioned previously. As stated earlier, the recombinants produced from a given Hfr $\times$ F— conjugation are nearly always F— in phenotype. The very last determinant to be transferred from Hfr to F—, however, is the factor that determines the Hfr donor state (a state in which genes are transferred at high frequency to F— recipients without converting the latter to the F+ mating type). Moreover, this determinant is the last one to be transferred by every Hfr strain. Since the Hfr state arises by mutation from an originally F+ state, one may imagine that the F+ $\rightarrow$ Hfr mutation is the result of the attachment of the F+ factor to some site of the chromosomal loop. The site of attachment is conceived to vary from one Hfr mutant to the next, but in any case it becomes the site where the loop is broken at conjugation, and the F+ end of the now linear chromosome is the trailing end during chromosomal transfer. Text Fig. 14 shows how this explanation, proposed by Jacob and Wollman, can account for the behavior of Hfr strains 1, 2, and 3 described above.

The F+ determinant is clearly different from the bacterial genes regularly carried by the chromosome. It is gene-like in that it determines a heritable alteration of the surface properties of the bacterium, such that conjugation bridges

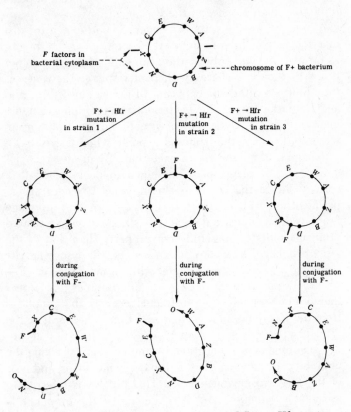

TEXT FIG. 14. The hypothetical origin of different Hfr strains.

will form specifically with F— cells. Nevertheless, the F+ agent appears to be capable of autonomous multiplication, for it can reproduce faster than the bacterial genome and, consequently, infect F— conjugants independently of the donor chromosome. Moreover, the F+ agent is extremely sensitive to cobalt and nickel ions or to the presence of acridine dyes. Treatment of an F+ population with one of these agents will leave most of the bacteria viable, but converted to an F— phenotype. Such F— mutants are highly stable, and never revert to an F+ condition unless reinfected with F+ agents by conjugation. Thus, the F— condition appears to be due to an *absence* of the F+ agent.

Although infectious, the F+ agent is not known to exist in a free, extracellular form like the bacteriophage. It infects, as far as is known, only by the conjugation bridge. Another property that F+ shares with bacteriophage, however, is the ability to alternate between an autonomous form and an integrated form. The bacteriophage multiplies autonomously during the lytic type of growth, but multiplies as an integrated part of the bacterial genome when it exists as a prophage in the lysogenized bacterium. By means of conjugation, the prophage may be shown to be attached to a specific site of the bacterial chromosome. Consider an experiment in which an Hfr strain carrying a mutant prophage is allowed to conjugate with an F— strain carrying a related prophage mutated in a different property than that of the Hfr's prophage. In a control experiment, the lysogenic Hfr strain is allowed to conjugate with a nonlysogenic F— strain. By interrupting mating at various times, one learns that a nonlysogenic F— recipient receives the prophage from the Hfr donor at a very precise time. The result of the transfer of prophage into an F— cell is to induce it to undergo autonomous replication, for the F— cell is lacking the immunity substance present in the lysogenic donor, and lysis of the F— exconjugant ensues. This process is referred to as *zygotic induction*, and it suggests that the prophage is linked to a certain site of the bacterial chromosome. Proof is furnished by the results of conjugation with the lysogenic F— bacterium. At the very time when prophage is known to enter the nonlysogenic F— recipient (i.e., by the time at which zygotic induction occurs), prophage is being transferred from lysogenic Hfr to lysogenic F—. In this case, the immune recipient is not lysed, but the receipt of the Hfr prophage is revealed by the *recombination of genes of the Hfr and F—* prophages, since the prophages carried by Hfr and F— are mutated in different respects, and recombination can take place between the resident prophage and the prophage introduced by conjugation. This demonstrable attachment of an integrated prophage to a specific site of the bacterial chromosome suggests that attachment to the bacterial chromosome underlies integration of the F+ agent. In the case of F+ integration, however, the site of attachment is not nearly as specific as that of integrated bacteriophages. Yet, as will be seen in the next section, bacteriophages vary in the specificity of their attachments to bacterial chromosomes. Thus, some bacteriophages are highly specific, attaching to only one site, while others have several possible sites of attachment, although some of the sites may be preferred over the others.

Although conjugation differs in several respects from transformation, it does effect, like transformation, a one-way transfer of genetic material from donor to recipient cell. The transfer, moreover, can be shown to involve DNA. The Hfr donor, or, alternatively, the recipient, can be labeled with tritiated thymidine in a manner similar to that discussed previously for P^{32}-labeled bacteriophage. The radioactive tritium (H^3) in the thymidine molecules finds its way almost exclusively into the DNA of the labeled cells. If the Hfr donor is labeled, tritium can be detected in an F— exconjugant. If the F— recipient is labeled, no tritium is detectable in the Hfr exconjugant. This experiment confirms the one-way nature of the transfer, and also reveals that it is DNA that is transferred, since the amount of tritium transferred is directly related to the amount of genetic material transferred. The average amount of DNA transferred, under usual conditions of conjugation, is equivalent to one-third of a nucleoid.

Labeling bacterial DNA with tritium has another great advantage. It permits a visualization of the DNA molecule. The tritium label is unstable, liberating β-particles of low energy. If the labeled DNA is extracted from the bacteria and deposited on a photographic film of appropriate sensitivity, the β-particles emitted upon radioactive decay will cause silver grains to be formed in their paths. The pattern of silver grains thus produced by the emitted particles reveals the form of the structure from which the β-particles were emitted. Thus, in a sense, the labeled DNA "takes a picture of itself," and the technique is therefore referred to as autoradiography. By autoradiography, John Cairns has recently found that the amount of DNA contained in a single nucleoid is disposed in the form of a single continuous loop (see Plate 3). It will be recalled that purely genetic considerations had already suggested that the *E. coli* "chromosome" is a single loop. All of the genetic markers of *E. coli* are mappable by conjugation on a single linkage group, and this linkage structure appears to be a loop (without ends), on the basis of the sequences of genes transmitted by different Hfr strains. Now the single loop of genes is found to have its physical basis in a loop of DNA. The loop is fragile, however, and can be converted into a single large filament, or several smaller filaments, by one or more "breaks" in the loop.

Modes of Genetic Recombination in Bacteria: Transduction

The attachment of bacteriophages to the chromosomes of their bacterial hosts appears to be the basis of another mode of genetic transfer. In 1952, Zinder and Lederberg discovered that nonlysogenic bacteria may be infected with some of the genes of lysogenic bacteria of the same species. This infection is mediated by the virus particles liberated spontaneously by a few bacteria in the lysogenic population, and it is referred to as *transduction*. Transduction is operationally distinct both from transformation and from conjugation. On the one hand, DNase does not prevent transduction, and on the other hand, cellular contact between donor and recipient bacteria is not required for transduction to take place. If the U-tube described in the previous section is employed, bacteriophage particles released by the lysogenic bacteria contained in one arm can pass through the bacterial filter and produce recombinant bacteria in the other arm.

Bacteriophages like P22 can transduce, but they cannot be "mapped." That is to say, no specific site of attachment can be found for them when one carries out the kind of conjugation experiments previously referred to. Correlated with this lack of a specific attachment site is the generalized nature of transduction executed by P22. This bacteriophage can transfer any gene from its previous host to its new host. However, like transformation, only one gene is usually transferred at a time, although some cases of linked transductions are known. Genes transduced together are generally adjacent to each other on the "map" constructed by conjugation experiments. The question arises whether *generalized transducing phages* have variable attachment sites in the hosts they lysogenize, so that as a group, they carry a variety of bacterial genes, although any one bacteriophage carries only that bacterial gene or genes to which it was adjacent during the temporary period of attachment.

Evidence in support of this interpretation of generalized transduction is furnished by studies of a different kind of transduction. Bacteriophages like λ can be "mapped," and when they transduce, they transfer only that restricted section of the bacterial chromosome to which they were affixed in the prophage state. Such region-limited transduction is termed *specific*, in contradistinction to the generalized variety. *Specific transducing phages* are obtained by inducing λ-lysogenized bacteria with ultraviolet light, and they are not found in spontaneous lysates. The role of the ultraviolet radiation will become clear in a moment. When λ prophage is "mapped," it is located close to the gene determining the galactose-utilizing character of the bacterium. It is significant, therefore, that the ultraviolet-induced lysate of λ-lysogenized bacteria transduces specifically the gene determining the galactose-utilizing character. However, it does so at the low frequency characteristic of generalized transductions, namely, with a frequency of 10^{-6} per phage particle. Thus, if a λ-lysogenic galactose-utilizing (*gal+*) bacterium is lysed by ultraviolet light, the LFT lysate thus obtained can transduce nonlysogenic *gal—* recipients with low efficiency. The *gal+* transductant is peculiar, however, for not only is it lysogenic for λ, but it is unstable. Every thousand generations, each transduced *gal+* bacterium produces unlike daughter cells. One is like the parent (unstably *gal+*), but the other is *gal—*, and stably so. Thus, the original *gal+* transductant is heterozygous for the *gal+* gene, which is dominant over its *gal—* allele. Stable *gal—* segregants that arise during cell division have lost the transduced *gal+* gene. If ultraviolet light is used to induce the lysogenic *gal+* transductants, a lysate is obtained with a much increased transducing efficiency. Therefore, it is called an HFT lysate, in contradistinction to the LFT lysate, for it transduces *gal+* determinants with a frequency of 50% per phage particle. The explanation for the difference between the LFT and HFT lysates turns out to be simple, although the experimentation necessary to verify it was quite ingenious. Without going into the experimental proof, it can be shown that the bacteriophage which specifically transduces the *gal+* gene is a defective mutant of the normal λ particle. The defective mutant lacks a portion of the viral genome, and in place of the lacking viral genome is substituted a portion of the bacterial genome to which it had previously been attached. How this deletion and substitution occur is still uncertain, but the evidence for their occurrence is substantial. The defective transducing λ arises initially as a result of ultraviolet irradiation of the *gal+*, λ-lysogenic bacteria. The frequency of these ultraviolet-induced mutants is low among the total number of phage particles in the lysate. This fact accounts for the low efficiency of the LFT lysate, and also for the lysogenic state of the *gal+* transductants, since practically every infection by a defective transducing λ particle is simultaneously accompanied by infection by a normal λ particle. Ultraviolet induction of the *gal+* transductants produced by an LFT lysate yields, on the average, one defective λ for every normal λ. Thus, there is a relative enrichment of the defective, transducing bacteriophages in the HFT lysate. Consequently, nonlysogenic *gal—* recipients can be infected by single bacteriophage particles from an HFT lysate, and a high yield of *gal+* transductants can be recovered. As is to be expected, the *gal+* transductants produced by single infection from an HFT lysate show defectively lysogenic properties. They are immune to superinfection by normal or defective λ, indicating that the genes controlling the production of the immunity substance are contained in the *gal+* transductants. However, these transductants cannot be induced to produce mature λ particles. This then is the nature of the defect in the transducing λ particle: Some step in the sequence of biochemical steps involved in autonomous replication is blocked. The *gal+* transductants produced by single infection are not only immune to superinfection by λ, but they are also unstable; they produce stable, nonimmune segregants about every thousand generations. Thus, the defective λ particle is lost periodically. The stable segregants thus produced are usually *gal—*, meaning that the *gal+* gene is lost, together with the defective λ particle which introduced it into the original transductant. Sometimes, however, the stable, nonimmune segregant is *gal+*, which means that, prior to loss of the transducing particle, a recombination must have occurred between the *gal+*, defective λ particle and the *gal—*, λ— bacterial genome so as to produce the *gal—*, defective λ particle that is subsequently lost. The picture we have of specific transduction is, therefore, the following. When a specific transducing particle enters the bacterium, it becomes attached to a specific site of the bacterial genome determined by the gene carried by the transducing particle. There is, in other words, a coming-together of homologous materials. The transducing particle in this state is said to be integrated, because it is replicated in synchrony with the bacterial genome; thus, the daughter bacteria produced by division each get a copy of the original transducing particle. The attachment of transducing particle to bacterial chromosome is intimate enough to permit occasional recombinations between them. The attachment, however, is not so stable that the particle (recombined or unchanged) cannot be lost as the result of an occasional accident of cell division.

Specific transductions reveal in a dramatic way the intimate nature of the interactions possible between virus and host. But how can we reconcile the difference between generalized and specific transducing phages? The answer seems to lie with phages like P1 which are capable of both stable and unstable transduction. The kind of transduction arising with this phage depends uniquely on the extent of homology between the gene being transferred and the genetic material of the recipient bacterium. Although the matter is still far from being definitely settled, it seems as though generalized transductions result from phages which have variable, transient sites of attachment to the bacterial chromosome and are stable when the probability is high that attachment will be immediately followed by recombination and insertion into the bacterial chromosome. The manner of attachment of prophage DNA to the bacterial chromosome is not fully understood, although it is obviously of great significance in the events associated with viral infection. That the attachment is of major importance to the consequences of infection is manifested in *abortive* transductions. With a generalized transducing bacteriophage like P22, many transductions are aborted for every transduction that is established as a stable clone. The abortion is revealed by the fact that the transducing particle, including the bacterial gene it carries, is not integrated into the recipient's genome. Instead of being replicated, it is passed along, during bacterial division, to only one daughter cell. Thus, the abortively transduced clone never contains more than one bacterium carrying the transduced gene. Nevertheless, it is possible to detect such clones, under certain circumstances. What factors affect attachment and integration are not known, but they play a key role in determining whether infection by a transducing phage is followed by a stable insertion of genetic material in the host's chromosome.

Transduction, like conjugation and transformation, is a one-way transfer of genetic material. The transfer also clearly involves DNA, since this is the principal bacteriophage substance injected into the bacterium when the mature, extracellular bacteriophage is absorbed to the bacterial wall.

Modes of Genetic Recombination in Bacteria: Sexduction

Both virus and fertility factor are seen to exist in two possible states in the bacteria they infect. They are capable of an autonomous mode of existence, in which they replicate independently of the host chromosome; alternatively, they may be integrated as a result of some specific attachment to the host chromosome in which case they replicate in synchrony with the host chromosome. When integrated prophages are induced to switch to an autonomous mode of replication, they may carry with them that part of the host chromosome to which they had been attached. This association of bacterial genes with viral genome is the basis of transduction. Can fertility factors also carry portions of the bacterial chromosome to which they had been attached? The fact is that they sometimes do carry bacterial genes, and, when they do, they are capable of transferring by infection the specific genes they carry. Such transfer of bacterial genes through the vehicle of fertility factors is called sexduction. One finds such gene-carrying fertility factors under interesting circumstances. Suppose one mates an Hfr strain of known genetic constitution with an F— strain of different genetic constitution. One then looks for "precocious recombinants"; these are rare zygotes that have received some specific Hfr gene* considerably earlier than would be expected from the known temporal sequence of transfer of Hfr genes to the F— recipients. These rare, precocious recombinants have entirely different properties from those obtained in the normal course of events. They generally contain only the Hfr gene that was looked for, although it is possible to find precocious recombinants for any one of a wide variety of Hfr genes. Like the bacteria produced by infection with specialized transducing phages, these recombinants are partially heterozygotic; they contain at once the introduced Hfr gene and the homologous allele that had been in the F— genome prior to conjugation. The introduced Hfr gene is physically associated with the F+ factor, however. The recombinant is phenotypically a donor, thus revealing the presence of the F+ factor, but the introduced gene is readily eliminated, along with the F+ factor, by the kind of treatment (exposure to cobalt ions or to acridine dyes) known to cause loss of fertility factors. The introduced gene may also be eliminated spontaneously, which occurs with the low frequency of once per thousand generations (per bacterium), characteristic of the loss of transducing particles in specialized transductions. In any case, when it is eliminated, the F+ factor is lost simultaneously. There is a clear case, therefore, for a physical association between fertility factor and bacterial gene in such sexductions. The sexducing particle is analogous with the specialized transducing particle; following infection, it is integrated (that is, it is reproduced in synchrony with the host genome), but the integration is not stable. As in the case of specialized transductions, the bacterial gene on the sexducing particle may be stably inserted into the bacterial chromosome as a result of recombination prior to loss of the F+ factor. If this happens, the allele of the introduced

---

* The expression "Hfr gene" is being used here as a convenient abbreviation for "gene derived from the Hfr parent."

bacterial gene is later lost with the fertility factor (see Plate 1).

Fertility factors, it will be recalled, differ from bacteriophages, in that they do not appear to occur in a free, extracellular form. They are bound to the cells they reside in, and they infect by way of the conjugation bridges they are responsible for forming. Despite this difference, fertility factors exhibit many of the unusual properties attributed to bacteriophage. They are not essential parts of bacteria, for bacteria can get along without them, but when residing in bacteria, they endow their hosts with specific hereditary characters. Inside their hosts they may replicate autonomously, or they may be integrated. Integration is correlated with attachment to the host chromosome. When the switch from the integrated to the autonomous state occurs, the fertility factor or the prophage may carry the specific region of the bacterial chromosome to which it had been attached. Fertility factors and bacteriophages form a class of genetic agents with distinct properties. Such genetic agents have been termed *episomes*, and bacterial geneticists are now searching for other possible examples of genetic factors behaving as episomes.

Episomes are of great interest for a number of reasons. First of all, because of the partially diploid condition they set up, episomes permit us to carry out certain kinds of genetic analysis which might otherwise not be possible. Examples of such analysis will be described later. Secondly, they permit an unusual kind of gene flow through individuals of the same species, and as we shall see later, between individuals of different species—episomes not being completely restricted in the species they infect. Finally, they lead us to wonder about the possible role they may play in the bodies of multicellular organisms. We would do well, therefore, to reconsider the episomes after we have had an opportunity to examine the contributions made by microbial genetics to our understanding of the structure and function of the genetic material of living things.

CHAPTER III

THE STRUCTURE AND REPLICATION OF GENETIC MATERIAL

The brief survey of the ways in which genetic material is disassembled and recombined in microorganisms has made at least one thing clear. There is no single way in which genetic recombination may occur; on the contrary, the modes of recombination are diverse. Yet despite the diversity, the biological role of recombination is served in every case. New combinations of genes are produced, assuring a greater genotypic variety than mutation itself would provide. It is not difficult to imagine that the variety produced through mutation and recombination is tested in a variety of environmental situations, and those gene combinations that confer survival and reproductive advantages on their bearers became predominant. In this respect, genetic recombination in microorganisms differs hardly at all from the same phenomenon occurring in the higher plants and animals. The distinctive feature of genetic recombination in the more complex forms of life is that it is usually incorporated within the reproductive process. In sexually reproducing animals and plants, for example, reproduction cannot occur without recombination already having taken place, for genetic recombination is assured in the very acts of fertilization and gamete production. Every generation must include individuals with new combinations of genes. In microorganisms, however, reproduction does not require concomitant recombination. In molds, for example, asexual reproduction assures continuity of the species, and sexual reproduction may occur only under special, restricted environmental conditions. In the bacteria, asexual fission (cell division) assures biological continuity, and gene transfers between individuals resulting in recombination is distinct from reproduction. It is tempting to speculate that microorganisms experimented with many processes involving genetic recombination before a highly successful mechanism, assimilated into a sexual mode of reproduction, became established in the evolutionary pathway leading to the advanced plants and animals.

The great contribution made by the study of genetic recombination in microorganisms does not lie, however, in the diverse patterns observed. It lies rather in the revelation of the chemical nature of genetic material. As a matter of fact, the first evidence geneticists possessed as to what genes were composed of came from the exciting discovery of DNA's role in bacterial transformation. In transformation, DNA was a conveyor of genetic information. Subsequently, DNA was found to be the substance transferred in bacterial conjugation. In the cells of higher plants and animals, DNA is found almost exclusively in the chromosomes, where it is duplicated during cell division. DNA, moreover, is halved in amount within the nucleus as a consequence of meiosis, and restored to the diploid amount following fertilization. No other constituent of the nucleus is so exactly duplicated and halved during mitosis and meiosis, respectively. There seems little doubt, therefore, that DNA is the chemical substance of genes, and were we to know the structure of DNA we should know how this substance is capable of storing and transmitting the directions for carrying out the complex system of chemical reactions that occur in the living organism.

Fortunately, a great deal of progress has been made in the elucidation of the structure of DNA. Before considering the current status of our knowledge on this subject, it will be worthwhile to understand two other powerful contributions made by microbial genetics, since they bear on the question of gene structure and function.

Selective Systems for Detecting Rare Mutations and Recombinations

One of the contributions has been briefly mentioned in the preceding section. It concerns the development of techniques for detecting rare genetic events. An advantage afforded by the use of microorganisms is the formulation of media in which mutant individuals are distinct from the normal, or wild-type individuals in a population. The wild-type *E. coli* bacterium cannot grow and reproduce in a medium containing the antibiotic streptomycin. Rare, streptomycin-resistant mutants in a predominantly sensitive population can reproduce in the presence of this antibiotic. It suffices to add streptomycin to the regular growth medium of *E. coli* to eliminate all but the resistant mutants, to *select,* in other words, the resistant mutants. Consider now a rare mutant of *E. coli* that is incapable of growing in the regular growth medium, but can grow in a medium supplemented by some specific substance, say an amino acid. (How are such mutants discovered in the first place? There obviously must be tricks to detect such mutants requiring specific growth factors. Suffice it to say, by arranging conditions so that growing bacteria are killed and nongrowing ones survive, a relative enrichment of nongrowing mutants can take place. Such conditions are available by the use of agents like penicillin that selectively eliminate actively multiplying cells.) A reverse mutation back to the wild-type condition can occur, and these reversions are easy enough to select. The technique in this case consists in *eliminating* from the medium the specific factor required for growth of the mutant; only the reverted cells survive and give rise to descendants.

Not only may these techniques be employed for detecting mutations, they may be utilized as well for detecting rare recombinations. Suppose two mutants, incapable of growing in the absence of tryptophan, have been independently acquired in a particular bacterial species, and one wants to know whether the two mutations occurred at identical sites of the genetic material in this species. One may "cross" the two mutants in a variety of ways, depending on the species being studied. If the species is the mold *Neurospora crassa,* the two mutants may be crossed sexually. If ascospores are obtained which are wild type in genetic constitution, the two mutations obviously occurred at different sites—specifically, at sites separable by genetic recombination. In bacteria, one mutant may be allowed to undergo conjugation with the other—or one mutant may be transformed with DNA from the other—or one mutant may be treated with bacteriophage carrying the mutated gene of the other strain. In any case, one looks for wild-type recombinants. Moreover, recombinants may be quite infrequent, yet detectable so long as a medium is available that selects for the recombinants.

We are indebted largely to George Beadle and Edward Tatum for revealing the immense power of the selective systems possible with microbial cultures. They were responsible for showing, in the early 1940's, that *Neurospora crassa* could grow in a defined, synthetic medium consisting of a number of inorganic salts plus a simple sugar like glucose plus one organic vitamin, biotin. The mold could grow also in a more complex medium consisting of all the known amino acids, vitamins, and other organic compounds found in the cells of living things. Growth in the relatively simple medium shows, however, that *Neurospora* can synthesize all the amino acids needed to manufacture its proteins, all the vitamins needed as cofactors of enzymes, indeed, all the building-blocks of lipids, polysaccharides, and nucleic acids, starting from the simple ingredients of the defined medium. By the use of X-rays to stimulate the production of mutations and the patient testing of many strains descended from irradiated spores, Beadle and Tatum were able to amass a very large collection of nutritionally deficient mutants. These were mutants that could *not* grow in the simple, defined medium. Again, by a patient program of testing, each mutant could be characterized as deficient in the synthesis of some single, specific substance essential for the growth of the organism. Some mutants were incapable of synthesizing the amino acid arginine, or tryptophan, or histidine, and so on. Others could not synthesize thiamine (vitamin B_1) or pyridoxal (vitamin B_6), or adenine, etc. A mutant could grow in the defined medium if one added the single required substance it could not synthesize.

Beadle and Tatum, and later a large group of collaborators, then undertook a twofold task. The first was to analyze the mutants genetically. In particular, it was important to know whether independently obtained mutants requiring the same substance for growth were genetically identical or not. The second job was to analyze the mutants biochemically. To what biochemical defect could the requirement for a specific growth substance be ascribed? By crossing each of the mutants with the wild-type strain, it was possible to learn that most of the mutants possessed a single recessive mutation in place of the normal dominant gene. Reference to Text Fig. 11 will help to recall that this conclusion is based on the finding of wild-type and mutant ascospores in a 50:50 ratio. By next crossing one mutant with another, it could be learned whether the mutations in the two strains were separable by recombination, and hence located at different sites of the genetic material. Let us consider the results of crosses made between various mutants requiring tryptophan for growth in the defined medium; these results typify what was observed with the other nutritionally deficient mutants. Some pairs of tryptophan-requiring mutants when crossed with each other yielded ascospores all of which were tryptophan-requiring. These mutants must therefore have contained identical mutations or mutations

so similarly located on homologous chromosomes that recombination between them was a rare event. Other pairs of
tryptophan-requiring mutants when crossed with each other
yielded a very high proportion of wild-type ascospores.
These mutants must have had their respective mutations
located at separate sites of the genetic material. Indeed,
from the proportions of wild-type, doubly mutant, and sin-
gly mutant ascospores, it could be ascertained that the mutations were inherited independently of each other. In this

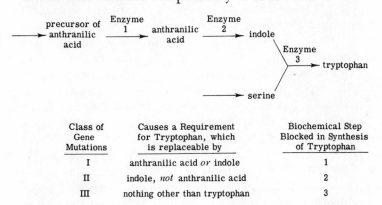

Class of Gene Mutations	Causes a Requirement for Tryptophan, which is replaceable by	Biochemical Step Blocked in Synthesis of Tryptophan
I	anthranilic acid *or* indole	1
II	indole, *not* anthranilic acid	2
III	nothing other than tryptophan	3

TEXT FIG. 15. Specificity of the mutations causing biochemical
deficiencies. Example: tryptophan-requiring mutants. The enzyme
coupling indole with serine to form tryptophan is known as tryptophan synthetase.

way, three classes of tryptophan-requiring mutants became
readily discernible; members of the same class possessed
mutations located at similar sites—sites which were, however, different from those of the mutations occurring in the
members of the other two classes.

The investigation of the biochemical blocks suffered in
the three classes of tryptophan-requiring mutants proved to
be very illuminating. First of all, it was learned that tryptophan is synthesized by the wild-type mold through a series
of steps, the last three of which are indicated in Text Fig. 15.
Typical of the biosynthesis of all essential metabolic sub-

stances within cells, tryptophan results from a chain of reactions, each of which is catalyzed by a specific enzyme.
The tryptophan-requiring mutants are characterized by a
defect in one of these reactions, and mutants belonging to
the same genetic class are characterized by a defect in the
same specific step. Thus, mutants of Class I are similar to
each other in that they can grow if tryptophan is replaced
by either indole (the immediate precursor of tryptophan)
or anthranilic acid (the precursor of indole). Mutants of
Class II tend, on the other hand, to accumulate anthranilic
acid in the medium in which they are growing, and they
can grow if tryptophan is replaced by indole, but not if it is
replaced by anthranilic acid. Finally, mutants of Class III
tend to accumulate indole, and tryptophan cannot be replaced as a growth requirement by either indole or anthranilic acid. To what are these specific defects due? Since each
of the steps in the synthesis of tryptophan is catalyzed by a
specific enzyme, the logical defect to look for was in the enzyme catalyzing each step. Biochemical analysis quickly
demonstrated that the block in the specific biosynthetic step
characteristic of a mutant class was indeed ascribable to the
absence of a functional enzyme catalyzing that step. Thus,
for example, extracts prepared from wild-type *Neurospora*
yielded an enzyme, called tryptophan synthetase, which can
couple indole with serine. Preparations made according to
a similar procedure from Class III mutants failed to possess
tryptophan synthetase activity.

Similar genetic and biochemical studies of the various
types of nutritionally-deficient mutants of *Neurospora* provided the same conclusion: Each genetic class of mutants is
blocked in some single biochemical reaction, which is ascribable to lack of activity of the enzyme catalyzing that reaction in the normal organism. This kind of combined genetic
and biochemical analysis appeared to be so fruitful that
similar techniques were adopted for yeasts and for various
species of bacteria. It was soon learned that the pathways
by which metabolic substances are synthesized are quite

PLATES 1-6

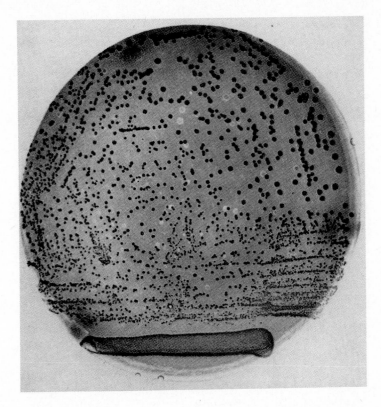

PLATE 1. Bacterial colonies in a Petri dish. *Escherichia coli* bacteria produced by sexduction were spread on the surface of EMB lactose agar. These bacteria are heterozygous (*Lac—/Lac+*) for the gene that permits utilization of lactose as an energy source. The lactose-utilizing cells form dark colonies. The few clear colonies are *Lac-* haploid segregants. [From F. Jacob and E. L. Wollman, "Sexuality and Genetics of Bacteria." Academic Press, New York, 1961.]

PLATE 2. Conjugation of bacteria. Stereoscopic electron micrograph of conjugating *E. coli* (Hfr K12 × F— C) bacteria. Note that the bacteria are connected by a thin bridge. Notice also the difference between the Hfr K12 bacterium, which is elongated, undergoing division and has a few long flagella, and the F— C bacterium, which is small and plump. [From F. Jacob and E. L. Wollman, "Sexuality and Genetics of Bacteria." Academic Press, New York, 1961.]

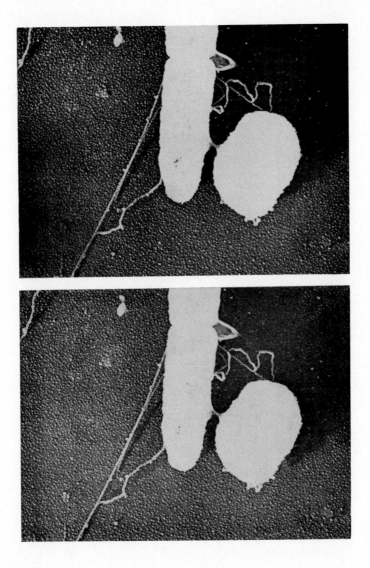

PLATE 3. The DNA-chromosome of the bacterium. *Escherichia coli* K12 Hfr bacteria were labeled with tritiated thymidine for two generations. The DNA-chromosomes were then extracted with lysozyme and autoradiographed. Inset, the same structure is shown diagrammatically and divided into three sections (A, B, and C) that arise at the two forks (X and Y). The forks are believed to result from replication of the chromosomal loop. [From J. Cairns, The chromosome of *Escherichia coli*. *Cold Spring Harbor Symposia for Quantitative Biology*, **28**, 44 (1963).]

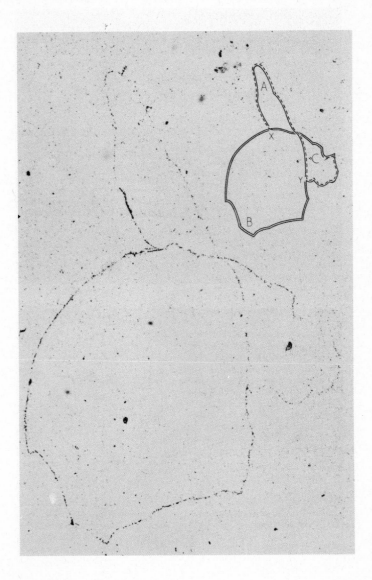

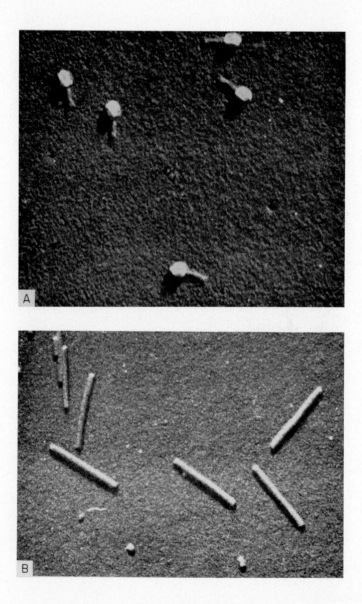

PLATE 4. The morphology of various viruses.
Part A: Particles of T2 bacteriophages. Magnification: 60,000 ×.
Part B: Tobacco mosaic virus particles. Magnification: 90,000 ×.

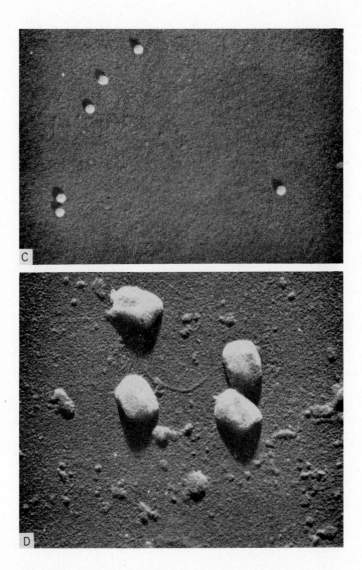

PLATE 4. Part C: Tomato bushy stunt virus, freeze-dried. Magnification: 81,828 ×.

Part D: Vaccinia virus. Magnification: 45,000 ×. All electron micrographs by Dr. R. C. Williams. [From R. Thomas, Viruses. *In* "The Cell" (J. Brachet and A. E. Mirsky, eds.), Vol. IV, Chapter 1. Academic Press, New York, 1961.]

PLATE 5. Electron microscopy of the cell.

Part A: Electron micrograph showing the adjacent halves of two parenchymal cells of the rat liver. Magnification: 12,500 ×. Nuclei (N), Golgi components (G) and mitochondria (m) are all indicated. Lysosomes (e) hover around a bile canaliculus (bc). The endoplasmic reticulum appears in two forms. In one the profiles are long, arranged more or less parallel in groups and coated with small particles (erg); this is the ergastoplasmic form of the endoplasmic reticulum. In the other, which is continuous with the first, the profiles are short and agranular or smooth (ers). These represent sections through the tubular elements of an irregular lattice. The rough and smooth distinction cannot be made at this magnification. Apart from these elements the cytoplasmic matrix shows a more or less homogeneous to finely fibrous composition.

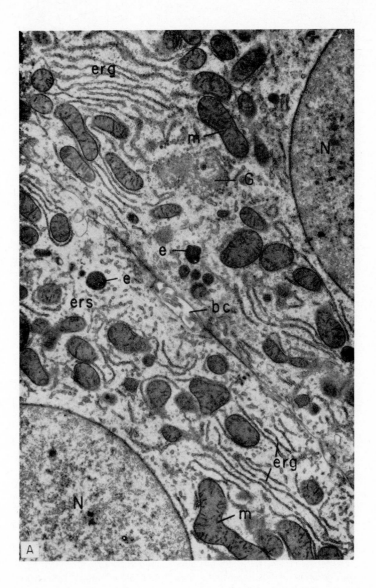

PLATE 5. Part B: Electron micrograph of ergastoplasm in rat liver cell. This is the typical image of the granular or rough forms of the endoplasmic reticulum (er) in the cells. The long slender profiles are made up of two parallel lines separated by a narrow space, and they represent vertical sections through vesicles of a flat or lamellar form. The outer surfaces are studded with small dense particles—the ribosomes. A few similar particles can be seen in the cytoplasmic matrix which lies between the lamellar units. Mitochondria are at m. Magnification: 40,000 ×.

Part C: Electron micrograph of another part of a rat liver cell showing the nuclear envelope and associated elements of the cytoplasmic ground substance. The double membrane structure of the nuclear envelope is similar to the profiles of the er in the neighboring cytoplasm. The outer surface of the nuclear envelope is coated with ribosomes. At points indicated by arrows (and at other places), there are profiles of pores through the envelope at which points the cytoplasmic matrix and nucleoplasm are in continuity. Magnification: 25,000 ×. [From K. R. Porter, The ground substance. In "The Cell" (J. Brachet and A. E. Mirsky, eds.), Vol. II, Chapter 9. Academic Press, New York, 1961.]

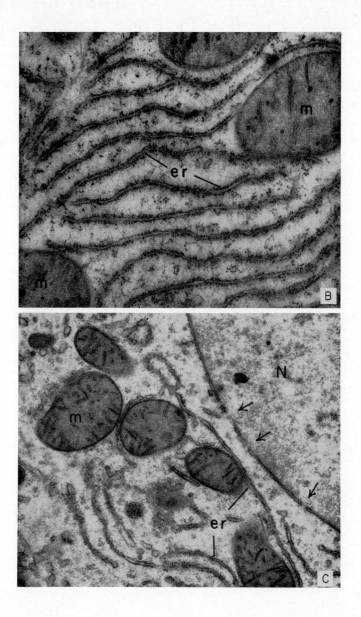

PLATE 6. The salivary gland chromosome. DNA-puffs in the fly *Sciara* as stained with azure A-Feulgen. Part 1: Portion of chromosome 2, showing subterminal DNA-puff near centromere end of chromosome, and large medial DNA-puff. Arrow points to position of RNA-puff, here shown as a slightly expanded area of low DNA concentration. (Magnification 1500 X.) Parts 2 and 3: Centromere end of chromosome 2 before and after DNA-puff formation. (Magnification 2200 X.) Part 4. Median puff, showing filamentous and granular compounds. (Magnification 2200 X.) [From H. H. Swift, Nucleic acids and cell morphology in Dipteran salivary glands. *In* "The Molecular Control of Cellular Activity" (J. M. Allen, ed.), Chapter 2. McGraw-Hill, New York, 1962.]

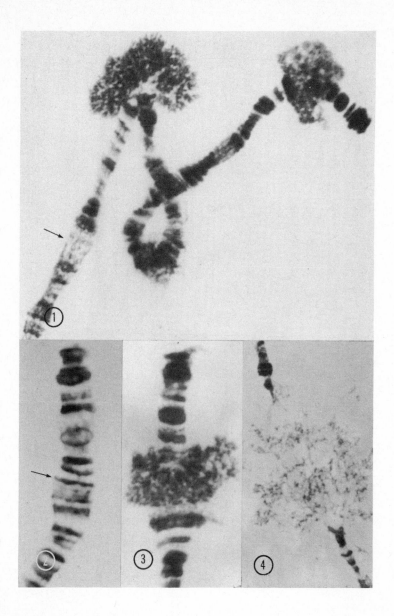

similar in the various kinds of microorganisms. As a matter of fact, when mammalian cells are studied biochemically, the synthetic steps are found to be similar to those discovered in microorganisms. This biochemical unity lends a great deal of confidence to the expectation that biochemical mechanisms uncovered in one group of organisms will prevail as well in other groups of organisms. Not only were similar biosynthetic pathways discovered in molds, yeasts, and bacteria, but the biochemical specificity of mutations appeared to be valid in all groups of organisms.

This conclusion came as no great surprise, merely as a dramatic and reassuring confirmation of a suggestion made in the early days of classical genetics. It will be recalled from our discussion of the relation of gene to character, in the first chapter, that evidence had been available as early as 1905 that human metabolic diseases due to gene mutations could be attributed to the absence of specific functional enzymes. The great value of microbial mutants was the variety of selective systems available to distinguish specific biochemical defects and the accessibility of microorganisms to biochemical dissection.

The Divisibility of the Gene

The very power of the microbial selective systems led to a breakdown of one of the tacit assumptions of classical genetics. The gene, it had been presumed, was a unit of the genetic material that functioned as a single entity in controlling some phenotypic character and responded as a whole to mutation and to recombination. The gene was conceived by classical geneticists as a particle with definite boundaries, joined together with other genes like beads on the chromosomal string, and that mutational changes in the gene always spanned the same boundaries as those that delimited the gene's function. In the classical view, moreover, the very same boundaries were always respected by the process of recombination. Thus, genes were separated from each other as particulate units, the boundaries of which were those of the functioning gene as well as of the mutational process. This view is entirely reasonable, although not necessitated by the evidence of classical genetics. Consider, for example, the case of mutations affecting the pigments of mammalian coats. In mammals, a common mutation results in an *albino* condition, which is characterized by the complete absence of pigmentation in the coat of the animal. Such animals, of course, are white or albino. There is another mutation causing a similar condition, referred to as *Himalayan albinism.* Himalayan albinos are unpigmented everywhere in their coats except for the extremities such as the tail, paws, eartips, and muzzle. If one crosses a complete albino, homozygous for its mutated albino gene, with a Himalayan albino, homozygous for its mutated gene, one obtains a heterozygous individual who possesses an albino mutation on one chromosome and a Himalayan albino mutation on the homologous chromosome. This heterozygous individual is Himalayan albino in phenotype, indicating that the Himalayan albino mutation is dominant in its expression to the albino mutation, as is the normal (unmutated) pigment-conferring allele. If one now crosses this heterozygous Himalayan albino with a homozygous complete albino, one could look for recombination between the two mutated loci in the heterozygote, which would occur during meiosis if the two mutations occurred at different (and nonoverlapping) sites on their respective chromosomes. Such recombinations would produce not only gametes containing a doubly mutated chromosome, but also gametes containing a fully wild-type chromosome. The production of wild-type chromosomes would be detected by the appearance of wild-type, pigmented progeny from the cross. Usually about 50 or so progeny, from several matings, are examined. No wild-type progeny are observed, and one concludes that the Himalayan albino and true albino mutations occur at identical sites and, hence, behave as alleles. But suppose the two mutations occurred at different, but very closely adjacent sites, such that the frequency of recombination between the sites was very low? It might require thousands or even millions of progeny to be examined to find the rare individuals that had received recombinant chromosomes. Thus, the resolution of mutated sites has a limit set by the number of progeny that can be readily examined. Nevertheless, the classical view—that the genetic units of function are indivisible by recombination—could be maintained until evidence proved otherwise. The evidence was soon forthcoming, especially with the use of bacterial and viral mutations.

Consider a class of mutants of *Escherichia coli* characterized by the lack of an active tryptophan synthetase. By means of conjugation or transduction, it is possible to show that the mutations involved in these mutants occur at very closely linked sites of the *E. coli* chromosome. In conjugation, each of the mutations is transferred from an Hfr donor into an F— recipient at about the same time. In transduction, each of the mutations is carried by the same transducing bacteriophage. Close as the mutations are located on the chromosome, however, they are separable. It is the dissecting tool of recombination that makes this demonstration possible. In a cross, for example, between a recipient *E. coli* carrying one of the mutations with a donor *E. coli* carrying a different one of these mutations (the cross may be carried out either by means of conjugation or transduction), a search may be made for rare recombinations between the mutated loci. Such recombinations will produce wild-type chromosomes, and the bacteria containing the recombinant chromosomes may be readily detected by inoculating the zygotic bacteria formed as a result of the cross into a medium lacking tryptophan; only the wild-type recombinants can grow and produce visible colonies. When such crosses are made, wild-type recombinants are indeed detected. They usually do not occur with as high a frequency as recombinations between mutations affecting different enzymes. Moreover, the actual frequency of recombination between mutations affecting the same enzyme depends on the particular pair of mutations being investigated in a given cross. The recombination frequency is a characteristic of each pair of mutations, and, like classical gene recombination, a linear map of the mutations can be constructed, based on the approximate additivity of the recombination frequencies of the various pairs. The important point is that extremely rare recombination events can be detected, recombination occurring with a frequency, say, as low as one per ten million zygotes produced. The lowest recombination frequency that can be detected is limited only by the spontaneous mutation rate. If the reverse mutation, tryptophan-requiring to wild-type, arises spontaneously in one out of every ten million bacteria in the population, it will be obviously impossible to distinguish a mutant from a recombinant when the frequency of the latter is as low as, or lower than 10^{-7}.*

Since mutations affecting the same enzyme are observed to undergo recombination, it follows that the region of the genetic material determining the structure of a given enzyme must be larger than the region capable of undergoing mutation or recombination. Mutation and recombination do not respect the boundaries that delimit a particular function of the genetic material. It was Seymour Benzer who brought this conclusion emphatically home in his analysis of over a thousand mutations affecting a single function of the bacteriophage T4. Suffice it to say, without going into a description of the kinds of experiments he performed, a new definition of the gene was required by his analysis. The gene was one thing if considered as a unit of function, another thing if considered as a unit of mutation or recombination. The results called for new, operational distinctions between the three properties of genetic material: its function in the metabolic chain of events in the cell, its mutability, and its ability to undergo recombination. To help keep these dis-

---

* The ability to resolve genetic sites by recombination can actually be increased further by the appropriate use of genetic markers on either side of the pair of markers undergoing recombination.

tinctions clear, Benzer proposed some new terms. The *muton* would be the smallest segment of the genetic material undergoing mutation, while the *recon* would be the smallest segment capable of undergoing recombination. It was hoped that the *cistron* would correspond to a unit of function, but it had to be defined operationally in a special way.

The cistron has the peculiar name it does because of the usual way in which geneticists determine whether two parts of the genetic material are involved in the same function. Two mutations are said to have caused an alteration in the same function if their wild-type counterparts fail to complement each other when present on different chromosomes within the same cell. Imagine, for example, a zygote heterozygous for two mutations, *a* and *b*. Let us indicate the wild-type form of the genetic material in the regions corresponding to either *a* or *b* as +. There are two possible ways of forming the heterozygote. The two mutations may be together on the same chromosome, so that one chromosome bears *a* and *b*, while the homologous chromosome bears the + alleles of *a* and *b*; in this case, the mutations *a* and *b* are said to be *cis* to each other or in the *cis* configuration. Alternatively, the two mutations may be on opposite chromosomes, so that one chromosome bears *a* and the + allele of *b*, while the homologous chromosome bears *b* and the + allele of *a*; in this case, the two mutations are said to be *trans* to each other or in the *trans* configuration. If a cell having two mutations in the *trans* configuration cannot carry out the wild-type function, but can do so if the mutations are in the *cis* condition, the two mutations may be said to belong to the same *cistron*. If, on the other hand, the wild-type function is carried out when the two mutations are in either the *trans* or *cis* configuration, the mutations are said to belong to different cistrons. The *cis, trans* test of whether two mutations can complement each other reveals the functional requirement for certain genetic sites to be adjacent to each other on the same structure. Being separated by the distance separating two chromosomes may be sufficient to prevent wild-type sites from completing their normal function. This finding indicates the need for physical continuity of wild-type genetic material, at least over a certain stretch, in order for a specific function to be executed. In support of this concept are the observations that mutations belonging to the same cistron are closely linked to each other as measured by recombination, and "map" as a cluster that *usually* (although far from invariably) fails to overlap sites of mutations belonging to different cistrons.

To what shall the term "gene" refer then? It is possible that a few cistrons may be involved in the fabrication of the same protein molecule. A protein molecule is, of course, very large, being composed of a large number of amino acids. Thus, cistrons adjacent to each other on the chromosome may be concerned with distinct segments of the same protein structure. We might, then, use the term gene to refer to the cluster of cistrons concerned with different segments of the same protein. In any case, if the term gene is to be used any longer, geneticists will have to agree, by convention, to use it only in a specified sense, lest they all become confused in their usage of the term. Henceforth, in this book, *gene* will be taken to mean the segment of genetic material determining some specific macromolecule found in the cell, and may consist of more than one cistron.

The studies of the chemical nature of the genetic material and the discovery of the divisibility of the functional units tell us a great deal. First of all, the genetic material is composed of DNA. Secondly, the structure of DNA must be such as to convey information about how certain cellular processes are carried out, and, more specifically, how the structures of certain protein molecules are to be generated. Finally, it must take a certain stretch of the DNA molecule to specify a protein's structure, and the processes of mutation and recombination must be able to make alterations *within* that stretch or segment of the molecule. Let us turn now to an examination of what has been learned about the structure of DNA, in order to see how well that structure meets the conditions that have just been set forth.

The Structure of DNA

In 1953, the American J. D. Watson and the Englishman F. H. C. Crick collaborated in a brilliant proposal which later earned them the Nobel Prize. They proposed a model for the structure of DNA which could account for the then known facts about this substance and which also made some very clear predictions about how it would behave under certain conditions. The facts that Watson and Crick had to go on may be briefly summarized as follows:

1. The molecule of DNA is very large in size. Determinations of the molecular weight of DNA extracted from various sources gave fairly similar results. Today we know that the DNA molecule is easily fragmented, and that the molecular weights estimated in 1953 were perhaps too low by a factor of 100 to 1000, because the DNA had been fragmented extensively during the process of purification. Nevertheless, the estimates then given ranged from 10^6 to 10^7. It was clear that DNA molecules were the largest of the biological macromolecules, for few protein molecules attain a molecular weight of 10^6. As a yardstick for comparison, an amino acid like tryptophan, which consists of 11 carbon atoms, 2 nitrogen atoms, 3 oxygen atoms, and 12 hydrogen atoms, has a molecular weight of slightly over 200.

2. Solutions of DNA are highly viscous and have other properties, such as birefringence, which indicate that the DNA molecules are in the form of long fibers. Such a shape would, of course, account for their fragmentability.

3. The DNA molecule is large because it is a polymer composed of a great many nucleotide units. A nucleotide is a molecule containing three parts: a purine or pyrimidine base linked to a 5-carbon sugar, which is linked, in turn, to a phosphate group. Deoxyribonucleic acid (DNA) is distinguished from another type of nucleic acid found in cells,

ribonucleic acid (RNA), by the nature of the 5-carbon sugar. In the case of DNA, this sugar is deoxyribose, whereas in the case of RNA, it is the related sugar, ribose. Because of this difference, DNA may be said to be composed of deoxyribonucleotides, RNA of ribonucleotides. Since the sugar and phosphate portions are similar from one deoxyribonucleotide to another, the differences between deoxyribonucleotides lie in the purine and pyrimidine bases. Only two purines are found in DNA or RNA, adenine and guanine. Only two pyrimidines are commonly found in DNA, thymine and cytosine, although two analogues of cytosine, 5-methylcytosine and 5-hydroxymethylcytosine, are found in small amounts in DNA from certain sources. In the case of RNA, thymine is absent, and the pyrimidine uracil takes its place. When DNA is digested by means of acid or treatment with the enzyme DNase, it is broken down into its individual deoxyribonucleotides. Since the molecular weight of a nucleotide is around 1000, there must be well over ten thousand nucleotides per DNA molecule. Prolonged digestion of DNA causes splitting of the deoxyribonucleotides formed initially, so that phosphate is split off (to produce base-sugar units called deoxyribonucleosides), and later, the bases are freed from the sugar components. From the manner in which the polynucleotide polymer is digested, the nucleotides are believed to be joined to each other in the fashion shown in Text Fig. 16: The bases stick out from the sugar-phosphate backbone of the polymer.

4. If one examines the DNA from a given species of organism, the proportions of the four bases, adenine (A), guanine (G), cytosine (C), and thymine (T), are constant, regardless of the kind of cell from which the DNA is drawn. On the other hand, the proportions vary from one species to another, so that they are characteristic features of the different species. A striking feature is always observed, however. The amount of guanine is equal to the amount of cytosine, and the amount of adenine is equal to the amount of thymine. The number of purines (A+G) is always matched

by the number of pyrimidines (T+C), while the relative proportion of the two purines (A/G), or of the two pyrimidines
(T/C), may vary widely from one species to another. The
ratio of the amounts of the bases characteristic of the
species is usually expressed in the form A+T/G+C.

5. The tendency for DNA molecules in high concentration to form fibrous aggregates makes it possible to examine such a fiber by means of X-rays. In the fiber, the
DNA molecules are oriented so that their long axes tend
to be parallel to each other. This has some of the features
of a crystal, so that techniques similar to those used for

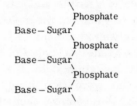

TEXT FIG. 16.   The polydeoxynucleotide strand.

determining the structure of inorganic crystals may be
applied for determining the structure of the individual
DNA molecule within the fiber. The technique consists in
determining the pattern in which X-rays are scattered
through the fiber or crystal. The wavelength of X-rays is
on the order of an Angstrom unit ($\text{A} = 10^{-8}$ centimeter),
which is smaller than some of the distances between atoms
in molecules. Consequently, the arrangement of the atoms
within a molecule can be determined from the X-ray scatter
or diffraction pattern, as it is called. The diffraction pattern
is observed as a pattern of spots on a photographic emulsion
on which the scattered X-rays are allowed to impinge.
Periodic spacings between the spots and the distances of
the spots from the center of the X-ray beam are related
to periodic distances between regularly arranged groups of
atoms within the molecule and to distances between atoms.

The X-ray diffraction patterns obtained with DNA fibers revealed a great deal of regularity, some of the periodic spacings being 34, 20, and 3.4 Angstrom units.

Watson and Crick constructed a model for the structure of the DNA molecule, which was consistent with the known facts of interatomic distances and atomic groupings in deoxynucleotides and polydeoxynucleotides, and with the kind of X-ray diffraction pattern actually obtained. This model also accounted for the remarkable equivalence that had been observed in the amounts of adenine and thymine, on the one hand, and in the amounts of cytosine and guanine, on the other, in DNA. Watson and Crick proposed that the DNA molecule is bipartite and has an over-all helical configuration. The two parts of the molecule are polydeoxynucleotidic strands wound around each other in a helical coil. The sugar-phosphate backbones of each strand are on the outside of the molecular helix and travel in opposite directions or, in other words, are of opposite polarity. The bases of each strand thus confront each other in the internal region of the molecule. The stability of the over-all configuration is achieved by hydrogen bonds formed between the bases confronting each other. In this model, adenine can pair only with thymine, guanine only with cytosine. The two strands of the Watson-Crick model are therefore *complementary*, in the sense that the sequence of bases along one strand specifies the sequences of bases along the other strand, although the relative amounts and order of the four bases along the molecule as a whole are not necessarily restricted. In this model, the periodic spacings observed in the X-ray diffraction pattern correspond to the distance between successive turns in the helix (34 Å), the diameter of the helix (20 Å), and the distance between successive nucleotides in each strand (3.4 Å). The principal features of the structure proposed by Watson and Crick are shown in Text Figs. 17 and 18.

The significance of the molecular model, however, does not reside exclusively in its compatibility with the data available to Watson and Crick. There are very interesting biological possibilities inherent in the proposed structure. First of all, the genetic information contained in a DNA molecule is seen to be the sequence of base pairs along the length of the molecule. Since the number of possible base sequences is equal to 4^n, where n equals the number of nucleotides per strand, an astronomical variety is possible to provide the genetic variety that exists, and is potential, within and between biological species. The Watson-Crick model, moreover, can account for the reproducibility of a particular sequence of bases in the DNA molecules of a given species. There would be no transmission of genetic information from parents to offspring—no inheritance, in other words—if the information inherent in a particular base sequence were not reproduced with great accuracy. The structure of DNA must therefore be carefully copied, or replicated, every time the cell reproduces. The DNA structure, as proposed by Watson and Crick, could be accurately replicated if the two strands of the helical molecule were unwound from each other under certain conditions of cell reproduction. Each separate strand could then serve as a *template for the production of its complement.* Free deoxynucleotides in the environment of the strand would be caused to pair, by hydrogen bond formation, specifically with their complementary deoxynucleotides in the strand. Thus an adenine base in a free nucleotide would pair with a thymine base in the DNA strand, a guanine base in a free nucleotide with a cytosine base in the DNA strand, and so on. The production of sugar-phosphate linkages between successive nucleotides arriving on the template would result in a double stranded DNA molecule in which the *new* strand had been specified by the *old*, template strand. Since each separate strand would serve as a template for the formation of its complement, two daughter molecules would arise identical to the parental molecule. In this view of DNA replication, however, every daughter molecule is half old, half new; only one strand has been newly synthesized in its entirety, while the other strand has been entirely conserved. This type of molecular replication has been termed *semiconservative*.

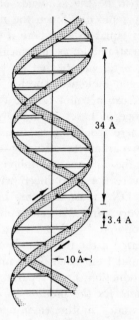

34 Å

3.4 A

←10 Å→

TEXT FIG. 17. Molecular model of DNA structure. The two helically coiled ribbons in this schematic diagram represent the two polydeoxynucleotidic strands in the molecule. The heavy arrows pointing in opposite directions indicate the opposite polarity of these two strands. The horizontal bars represent the *pairs* of bases (purine-pyrimidine) that confront each other periodically within the central area of the molecule. Certain of the molecular dimensions are shown: 34 Å—the distance between successive turns in a strand; 3.4 A—the distance between successive base pairs; 10 Å—the radius of the helix. From C. B. Anfinsen, "The Molecular Basis of Evolution." Wiley, New York, 1959.

Finally, the proposed DNA structure is also amenable to mutation. Although adenine in its usual or more probable state will pair best with thymine, adenine can occur with a low but definite frequency in an unusual, tautomeric form. In this tautomeric form, adenine pairs best with cytosine. Similarly, thymine can exist in a tautomeric form, which pairs best with guanine rather than adenine. The tautomeric forms of the various bases are due to the mobility of hydrogen atoms. With new positions of the hydrogen atoms, the kind of hydrogen bonds that may be formed is altered. In Text Fig. 19, the normal kind of base pairing through hydrogen bonds is contrasted with the

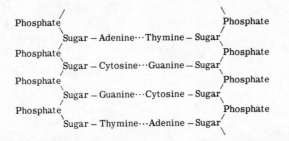

TEXT FIG. 18. Complementary bases in DNA. The helical coil of the DNA molecule is "unwound" in this figure in order to show the confrontation, in the central portion of the molecule, of the bases belonging to the polydeoxynucleotidic strands of opposite polarity. Note that the purine guanine complements the pyrimidine cytosine and that the purine adenine complements the pyrimidine thymine. The dotted line represents the hydrogen bonding between complementary bases.

less frequent or abnormal kind due to tautomeric shifts in the hydrogen atoms. Imagine that adenine occurs in a given position on one strand of a DNA molecule. Suppose a rare but possible shift occurs in this adenine to the imino form shown in Text Fig. 19. Should the tautomeric form of adenine arise just prior to DNA replication, the imino form of adenine will cause a cytosine to appear in the homologous position of the complementary strand that is produced. On subsequent DNA replications, the adenine on the one strand may return to its normal configuration, but the cytosine on the other strand will specify guanine to be paired with it. Thus, from an originally adenine-thymine pair, a guanine-cytosine pair will arise, and the change will subsequently be reproduced in a regular manner. Since genetic information resides in the sequence of bases, and since the sequence has been altered at one point, a mutation at a given point in the

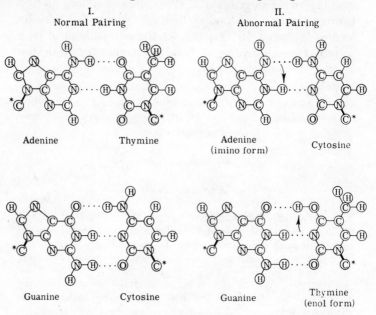

TEXT FIG. 19. Normal and abnormal base pairing in the DNA molecule. Pairing of a purine in one strand with a pyrimidine in the other strand of the double-helical DNA molecule is shown with the various atoms in their approximate relative positions. Hydrogen bonds are indicated by the dotted lines. The 1′ carbon atom of the deoxyribose residue is indicated by an asterisk. In II, the rare enol form of thymine and the rare imino form of adenine are shown; in these, the shift of the hydrogen atom is indicated by the arrow. This shift is responsible for the "abnormal" pairing.

DNA molecule has effectively occurred. The Watson-Crick model, therefore, accounts not only for the great accuracy of DNA replication, but also for the infrequent mistakes without which genetic mutation and potential diversity would be impossible.

The structure that Watson and Crick proposed for DNA had an enormous influence on the direction of research in molecular genetics. Experiments were devised to test the validity of the model. Results were not long forthcoming, and they were impressive in the collective weight of support they gave to the model. Purified DNA molecules were examined under the electron microscope, and they were found to have the shape of elongated fibers with a diameter of 20 Å, as the model would lead one to expect. Resolution with the electron microscope is not so powerful, however, to permit one to discern any double strandedness or much helicality within the fiber. However, it turned out that the DNA molecule loses its "rodlike" configuration, as a result of heating at high temperatures, and passes to a randomly coiled shape. This process is called *heat-denaturation*, and it takes place very abruptly as the temperature of the DNA solution is increased. The temperature at which the transition to the randomly coiled configuration occurs is generally much higher than that required for the denaturation and inactivation of proteins, and appears to depend on the relative quantity of guanine and cytosine in the molecule. As a result of heat-denaturation, it is significant that the molecular weight of the DNA molecule is about halved, and the diameter of the individual fibers seen in the coiled configuration is about half that of the native DNA fiber. The results are consistent, therefore, with the notion that heat-denaturation causes a separation of complementary strands of the DNA molecule. The hydrogen bonds between strands appear to be broken, so that the individual strands collapse into a random coil. If transforming DNA is used, heat-denaturation results in a loss of biological activity, which is apparently due to poor penetrability of the random coils into the recipient bacteria.

The effects of heat-denaturation can be reversed if the heated DNA solution is allowed to cool slowly rather than quickly. Not only are native, rodlike molecules reformed, but a considerable portion of the original biological activity is restored. The notion is that, under conditions of slow cooling, complementary base pairs have sufficient time to recognize each other and pair as in the native configuration. The reversal of heat-denaturation during slow cooling is called *renaturation*, and it does seem to require complementarity in the renaturing strands. The evidence for this conclusion comes from experiments in which transforming DNA is labeled with a stable isotope of nitrogen, N^{15}. The stable N^{15} is detected by the increased mass (and hence density) it gives to the DNA molecule. Labeling of the DNA is readily accomplished by growing bacteria in a medium containing nitrogen in the form of N^{15}. N^{15}-labeled DNA is readily distinguished from ordinary N^{14}-DNA by centrifugation in a so-called density gradient. This technique was first used by Meselson and Stahl to determine how DNA is replicated, and their experiments will be described shortly. The technique was later applied for the purpose now under discussion, namely for determining the mechanism of heat-denaturation and renaturation. If a solution of a salt such as cesium chloride (CsCl) is centrifuged at very high speeds for a long time, the individual salt molecules are distributed in the centrifugal field according to a gradient. The molecules tend to be less and less packed as the distance from the rotor's center is increased, and the density gradient is very uniform. The density gradient can be detected very easily. It suffices to centrifuge the cesium chloride solution in a plastic centrifuge tube, to puncture a small hole into the bottom of the tube after centrifugation, and to collect the drops that issue from the hole. The drops prove to be of uniformly decreasing density. The addition of a substance of unknown density to the salt solution prior to centrifugation will result in the packing of that substance's molecules within a specific band of the cesium chloride gradient produced after centrifugation. That band will be the one in which the density of salt molecules corresponds to the buoyant density of the substance in question. The narrowness of the band in which the substance is packed is inversely proportional to its molecular weight, macromolecules such as those of DNA packing in very narrow bands. The buoyant density of DNA can be increased to such an extent by N^{15}-labeling that the labeled DNA packs in an entirely separate band from ordinary N^{14}-DNA in a cesium chloride gradient. To return to the mechanism of heat-denaturation, the experiment can be performed in which N^{15}-labeled DNA is mixed with ordinary N^{14}-DNA. Prior to heat-denaturation, the labeled molecules are separable from the unlabeled ones. If one denatures the mixture and cools it quickly, two new bands are observable in the density gradient. These bands correspond to the densities of heat-denatured N^{15}- and N^{14}-DNA molecules, which are denser, respectively, than native N^{15}- and N^{14}-DNA molecules. If the mixture is denatured and then cooled slowly, an interesting change is observed. Three bands are observed in the density gradient, and they correspond, respectively, to native N^{15} and N^{14} molecules and to so-called "hybrid" DNA molecules, which are a composite of N^{15} and N^{14} strands. The existence of hybrid DNA is demonstrated by physically separating the three bands. The novel band proves to contain molecules which, when heat-denatured, yield two classes: heat-denatured molecules containing exclusively N^{15} or N^{14}. These are the kind of results achieved when N^{15}-DNA is mixed with N^{14}-DNA of the same species. A hybrid DNA is not always formed, however, if N^{15}-DNA is mixed with N^{14}-DNA from a different species. Whether or not a hybrid DNA is formed depends on how similar the two species of DNA are in over-all base content. The greater the similarity in their A+T to G+C ratios, the greater the tendency for hybrid formation. This finding supports the view, therefore, that renaturation of heat-denatured DNA molecules is the result of complementary base-pairing between single DNA strands.

The Replication of DNA

The advantage afforded by the techniques of density gradient centrifugation and heat-denaturation permitted Meselson and Stahl to study the manner of DNA replication.

The procedure was simple and elegant. *Escherichia coli* bacteria were grown in a medium containing nitrogen in the form of N^{15}, so that their DNA was thoroughly labeled with the nitrogen isotope. The bacteria were then removed

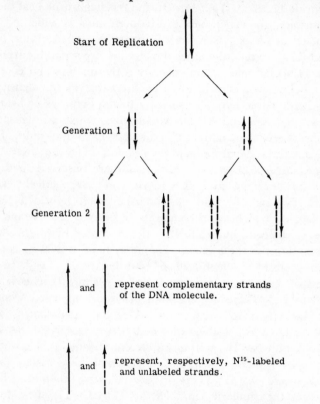

TEXT FIG. 20.   The mechanism of DNA replication.

to a medium containing nitrogen in its usual N^{14} form. At various times thereafter, samples of the bacterial population were removed, DNA extracted and examined in a cesium chloride gradient. When the bacteria doubled in number, their DNA was found to be of one type, namely, hybrid DNA. With each succeeding bacterial generation, however, the relative amount of hybrid (N^{15}-N^{14}) DNA diminished as normal (N^{14}-N^{14}) DNA increased in amount. Indeed, the fraction of the total DNA which was N^{15}-N^{14} hybrid DNA was exactly equal to 2^{1-n}, where $n =$ the number of bacterial generations that elapsed after removal of the N^{15}-labeled bacteria to an N^{14} medium. Thus, two generations after growth in an N^{14} medium, one-half of the molecules are hybrid; five generations afterwards, one-sixteenth are hybrid. The remainder of the molecules are all unlabeled. These results are entirely consistent with the suggestion inherent in the Watson-Crick model, that DNA replication is semiconservative. Text Fig. 20 illustrates how a double-stranded DNA molecule, labeled with N^{15}, will produce hybrid molecules in an N^{14} medium, if it replicates by a semiconservative mechanism. First generation DNA is uniformly half-labeled with N^{15}; DNA of subsequent generations continues to include half-labeled molecules, which constitute a regularly diminishing fraction of the DNA of the total bacterial population.

The *in Vitro* Synthesis of DNA

The results obtained by Meselson and Stahl showed that the DNA molecule is made up of two physically continuous subunits which are separated from each other, but individually conserved during the synthesis of new DNA molecules. Every newly synthesized DNA molecule contains one old, conserved subunit and one subunit which is entirely new. It was tempting to infer that the subunits demonstrated in the work of Meselson and Stahl corresponded to the complementary strands of the Watson-Crick model of the DNA molecule. But of course these experiments tell us nothing about the possible complementary nature of the subunits. Evidence on this question comes from an entirely different line of investigation.

Arthur Kornberg and his collaborators were instrumental in purifying from bacterial extracts an enzyme system that was capable of synthesizing DNA *in vitro*. The substrate

for the enzyme system is a mixture of the triphosphates of
the four deoxyribonucleosides commonly found in DNA,
namely, guanosine triphosphate (GTP), adenosine triphosphate (ATP), thymidine triphosphate (TTP), and cytidine
triphosphate (CTP), in which the bases are, respectively,
the aforementioned guanine, adenine, thymine, and cytosine.
Omission of any one of the deoxyribonucleoside triphosphates results in a drastic curtailment of the incorporation
of the entire group of deoxyribonucleoside triphosphates
into the final product. The product was a compound of
high molecular weight having all the properties of a native
DNA. Inorganic pyrophosphate, a diphosphate compound,
is also liberated, presumably by the splitting off of the
terminal diphosphates of the deoxynucleoside triphosphates
while they are being joined together into the DNA polymer.
The interesting feature of this DNA-synthesizing system is
its requirement of a primer. To get the synthesis under way,
a small amount of a priming DNA must be added to the
reaction mixture. The priming DNA can come from any
source, which does not even need to be related to the
source of the enzyme system itself. Thus, yeast or pneumococcal DNA can serve as a primer for the DNA polymerase,
as the enzyme is called, obtained from *E. coli.* The important discovery is that the proportions of bases in the final
DNA product depends on the proportions of bases in the
primer, not on the proportions of the four deoxyribonucleoside triphosphates placed in the reaction mixture (provided
the reactants are present in excess). In the DNA obtained
from various microbial sources, the A+T to G+C ratios
vary from as high as 1.85 to as low as 0.4. The DNA produced by the DNA polymerase has an A+T to G+C ratio
that is similar to that of the particular primer used. Moreover, by a technique that partially fragments DNA and
identifies the terminal deoxyribonucleotides in the fragments, a comparison can be made of the primer DNA and
the DNA product in terms of the relative frequencies with
which certain deoxyribonucleotides are adjacent to each

other in the same strand (an adenine-containing deoxyribonucleotide next to a guanine-containing deoxyribonucleotide, and so on). From the results obtained with this technique, it appeared that not only were the proportions of the
four bases in the DNA product similar to those of the four
bases in the primer, but the sequence of bases was very
much alike in the primer and product. This led to the conclusion that the priming DNA was actually serving as a
template which specified that the arrangement of bases in
the product would be like its own base arrangement. How
did the primer act as a template? To answer this question,
advantage was taken of the existence of an unusual bacteriophage. This is bacteriophage ϕX-174, which in its extracellular, mature form contains DNA in a single-stranded condition. Not only does the DNA from extracellular ϕX-174 lack
the usual base complementarity ($A = T$, $G = C$) found in
DNA, but its X-ray diffraction pattern is that to be expected
of single-stranded molecules. The DNA of ϕX-174, once
inside its bacterial host, replicates by a semiconservative
scheme, nevertheless, for the replicating, vegetative form
of ϕX-174, during its period of multiplication in the host, is
of the standard two-stranded, base-complementing variety.
The single-stranded DNA from mature ϕX-174 can serve as
a primer for Kornberg's enzyme system, and, when it does
so, causes the formation of the so-called replicating form of
ϕX-174, which is double-stranded and exhibits base complementariness. These findings support very strongly the
idea that the individual strands of the DNA molecule serve
as templates for the formation of their complements, and
that *in vitro* synthesis of DNA is as semiconservative as the
process occurring *in vitro*. It is not clear how the complementary strands unwind from each other periodically, as
they must if replication is to occur in this semiconservative
fashion. Presumably, some protein enzymes serve to unwind
the double helix as others transport the deoxyribonucleoside
triphosphates to the template surface. In any case, evidence
has been provided for the complementing basis of the tem-

plate's role in DNA synthesis. It is now clear that native, double-stranded DNA is not essential for priming the DNA polymerase. Not only will single-stranded ϕX-174 DNA work as a primer, but heat-denatured DNA from a variety of sources will serve as well. In any case, the system of enzymes that is called DNA polymerase appears to be highly accurate in the synthesis it executes for it synthesizes with considerable exactitude the complements of the nucleotide arrangements contained in the priming strands. Probably, therefore, the extracted DNA-synthesizing system is not an artifact, but a real part of the biological process of DNA replication in the living cell. Hopefully, DNA polymerase will soon be used *in vitro* to synthesize DNA with genetic activity, with the help of transforming DNA as primer.

The Cistron, Muton, and Recon in Molecular Terms

The picture of DNA synthesis seems pretty clear in its broad outline. Much more needs to be known, of course, about such important details as the reversible winding and unwinding of the complementary strands of the DNA molecule (particularly when the DNA is in the form of a closed loop). Nevertheless, the double-stranded nature of the molecule is clear, the complementariness of the two strands has been supported, and a semiconservative mode of replication has also received experimental confirmation.

The arrangements of the four deoxyribonucleotides in the DNA molecule is also obviously not a random affair. The proportions of these nucleotides and their sequence must have genetic significance, for they are characteristics of the various biological species and are reproduced accurately by the DNA-synthesizing system inside the cell. The conclusion seems warranted that the sequence of nucleotides in the DNA molecule determines the genetic function known to be performed by DNA. Can we then translate the units of genetic material that have been delineated by genetic analysis into particular nucleotide sequences? This is one of the important aims of current research in molecular genetics. Specific functions cannot as yet be assigned to specific nucleotide sequences, since methods are not yet available for analyzing the nucleotide arrangements of DNA in detail. There is good reason to expect that this problem will be solved in the not too distant future. One recent finding holds out much reason for optimism. The DNA in bacterial nucleoids appears to occur in a single, continuous piece; it may actually be physically circular, corresponding to the genetic circularity that has been deduced from the mapping experiments with conjugating bacteria. Such uniformity of cellular DNA certainly cannot occur in higher plants and animals, if for no other reason than that the DNA of different chromosomes must be different, to say nothing of the possibility that the DNA molecules within a single plant or animal chromosome may be separate and different. Nevertheless, the singleness of bacterial DNA may make it possible to obtain a uniform molecular sample to be analyzed in great detail. Differences between molecules will not be present to obscure differences within a molecule.

The single DNA molecule of the bacterial nucleoid is, in all likelihood, the bacterial chromosome, if we ignore the role of some hypothetical protein which may serve as a structural support for the DNA. It must be huge in size, having a molecular weight well over 10^8. This means that it contains over 10^5 nucleotide pairs. If these are strung out in a continuous, albeit helical chain, what are the demarcations of the individual genes? What are the mutons and recons? Speculation about the first question must be postponed to a later chapter, but something can be said here about the second question. Genetic analysis, described at the beginning of this chapter, informs us that the gene is certainly larger than the muton or recon. If a gene is the unit which specifies the arrangement of amino acids in a protein, and if, for reasons to be expounded further below, three consecutive nucleotide pairs in the DNA molecule specify a single amino acid in the protein molecule, then there will be three times as many nucleotide pairs in the gene as there are amino acids in the protein it specifies. Proteins vary in size, containing from one hundred to hundreds of thousands of amino acids. The different genes must then vary in size between these orders of magnitude.

The muton and the recon may, on the other hand, be no larger than a single nucleotide pair. The lowest frequency of recombination observed between two mutated sites of bacteriophage DNA, when related to the total number of nucleotide pairs in the DNA molecule, is consistent with the notion that the recon is as small as a single nucleotide pair. Recombination, in this view, can separate out a single nucleotide pair from a DNA molecule. As for mutation, it is quite plausible that a permanent change can be brought about at the level of a single nucleotide pair in the DNA molecule. The hypothesis that Watson and Crick suggested for mutation, that it consists in a change from an adenine-thymine pair to a guanine-cytosine pair, or vice versa, is in conformity with this view. According to this notion, therefore, the muton is also the individual nucleotide pair.

Let us turn now to an examination of mutation and recombination, to see how well the evidence of molecular genetics relating to these processes supports the elementary notions that have just been formulated.

CHAPTER IV

MUTATION AND RECOMBINATION OF GENETIC MATERIAL

The existence of genes could not be known if mutations did not occur. One might be able to infer, of course, that a hereditary mechanism of some kind assures that offspring develop characters similar to those observed in parents, but one would not be able to detect the separability of genetic structures concerned with different characters, unless those structures occasionally and independently underwent permanent changes, for without such heritable gene changes, or mutations, the specific character differences essential for breeding experiments would be lacking—to say nothing of the intellectual difficulties created by imagining how evolution could have occurred without a constant supply of genetic variation.

Mutations do occur, of course, and the separability of genetic structures controlling different cellular functions has been demonstrated. Mutations arise spontaneously, usually with quite low frequencies. This statement simply means that under the ordinary conditions in which organisms live, the chances are small, but finite, that events will transpire leading eventually to gene mutations. Obviously, it would be interesting to know something about the events that result in mutations. With such knowledge, we should be able to confirm our views about the structure of the genetic material and the manner in which it reacts with its immediate surroundings. The infrequency and randomness of spontaneous mutations make it impossible for the investigator to know precisely when and where a mutation will strike and, consequently, impossible to watch those particular events that produce mutational changes. An understanding of the mutational process, therefore, must depend on some alternative to a direct examination of the origin of spontaneous mutations. The strategy that geneticists have employed is to find agents that increase the frequency of mutations and to study the manner by which such *mutagens* work. By extrapolation to the "naturally" occurring situation, it should be possible to explain the occurrence of spontaneous mutation.

Theoretical Basis of Mutagenesis

In 1927, H. J. Muller, studying the fruit fly, and L. J. Stadler, studying corn, independently discovered the mutagenic effects of ionizing radiation. This discovery led to further investigations which showed that several kinds of radiation, including ionizing X-rays and ultraviolet light, could induce mutations in genes. While significant in demonstrating that the mutability of genes could be excited or enhanced by environmental alterations, radiation experiments were not too helpful in elucidating the physical and chemical basis of mutation. Unfortunately, there is a big gap between the exposure of whole organisms or their cells to radiation and the production of gene mutations. How direct, one may legitimately wonder, is the action of radiation? Are the genes the primary targets of the radiation, or do many chemical steps intervene between the first radiation-induced change in the cell and the ultimate gene mutation being studied? Directly or indirectly produced, what is the nature of the radiation-induced change of the gene's structure? This uncertainty does not necessarily mean that hypotheses were utterly lacking as to the mode of action of radiations.

Ionizing radiations, such as X-rays, were known to cause breaks in the chromosomal fiber, because they produced translocations and inversions (inverted gene sequences), as well as chromosomal fragments that were eventually lost to the cell. But X-rays also produced changes within single genes. How did these come about? Ultraviolet light, on the other hand, produces fewer chromosomal rearrangements, or losses, and more "point" mutations. Ultraviolet radiation is absorbed by various substances in the cell, including purines, pyrimidines, and nucleotides, but since many of these substances are found free in the cytoplasm, as well as incorporated into RNA and DNA polymers, much of the mutagenic action of ultraviolet light could be indirect, although some of its action could be direct. Actually, there is good evidence to believe that at least some of the mutagenic action of ultraviolet radiation occurs directly as a consequence of absorption by nucleotides in the DNA molecule itself.

Chemical substances of various kinds have also been found to induce mutations. The list of chemical mutagens is long, and many are chemically unrelated to each other, so that no common mode of mutagenesis can be readily invoked. The apparent validation of the Watson-Crick model of DNA permits us to be somewhat more rational now in the investigation of chemical mutagens. The model, for example, suggests that whatever increases the likelihood of tautomerism of the bases in the DNA molecule should be mutagenic. Moreover, bases that are chemically related to the bases known to occur in DNA might be expected to replace the natural bases occasionally. If such chemically related, unnatural bases, or base analogues, as they are called, have a greater tendency to tautomerize, they might bring about an increase in the spontaneous mutation rate after they have been incorporated into the DNA molecule. Still other agents might have specific affinities for nucleic acids and react in predictable ways to cause changes in base structure. Such agents would also be mutagenic. A rational procedure would consist, therefore, in examining chemical agents of known structure and reactivity such that they would be likely candidates as chemical mutagens. In recent years a great deal of progress has been made in understanding mutagenesis by adopting such a procedure.

Let us consider first of all what the Watson-Crick model of DNA structure would predict for certain mutagens. It will be recalled from the previous chapter that Watson and Crick proposed that spontaneous mutation arises as a result of a tautomeric change in a base in one of the two strands of the DNA molecule. As a consequence of the semiconservative mode of DNA replication, therefore, a molecule containing a base change in one strand will give rise to two daughter molecules, one of which will be unmutated, while the other will be mutated. The molecule in which the original mutational event occurs is conceived, therefore, to be a *mutational heteroduplex*, capable of generating not a uniform progeny of mutated molecules, but a mixed progeny of mutated and unmutated molecules. This prediction of the Watson-Crick model is illustrated in Text Fig. 21. For the purpose of simplicity in this figure, the original mutational event is indicated by a cross. In effect, however, the cross represents a change in a base of a single nucleotide, such that its pairing affinities are altered. Reexamination of Text Fig. 19 will reveal what would be expected if the cross were, in reality, a change from the amino form to the imino form of adenine, or a change from the keto form of thymine to the enol form. In the former case, at the level of the nucleotide pair where the tautomeric shift occurred, replication of the DNA molecule would result in a *transition*, in one of the daughter molecules, from an adenine-thymine pairing to a pairing between the imino form of adenine and cytosine. In the subsequent replications of this mutated daughter molecule, the imino form of adenine would probably return to its usual amino form, but the strand containing cytosine, where thymine used to be, would persist and specify complementary strands possessing gaunine in place of adenine. In the case in which the normal keto form of thymine shifts to the abnormal enol form, a similar kind of transition would lead eventually to the permanent replacement of an adenine-thymine pair by a guanine-cyto-

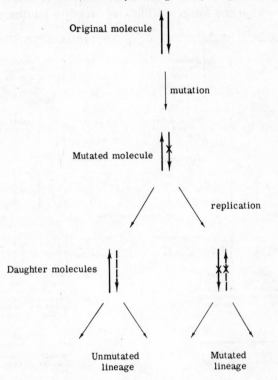

TEXT FIG. 21.   The origin of mutation in a DNA molecule: the mutational heteroduplex. Arrows in opposite directions indicate complementary strands. Dashed lines represent newly synthesized strands. A cross represents a base change at a single nucleotide position in *one* of the strands of the DNA molecule.

sine pair. These two cases are schematically summarized in Text Fig. 22. The Watson-Crick model thus predicts two properties of mutation: first, its origin in a heteroduplex molecule; second, a transition from one complementary base pairing, such as A--T, to another complementary base pairing, such as G--C. Chemical mutagens might be expected to act, therefore, by promoting base pair transitions. An action of this kind could conceivably come about either by exciting the intrinsic ability of bases to tautomerize or

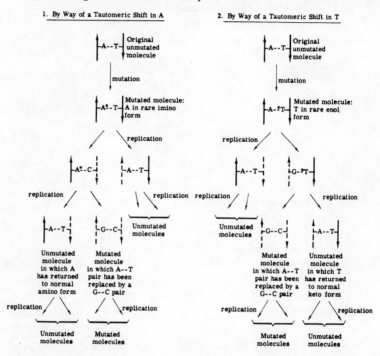

TEXT FIG. 22. The origin of mutation in a DNA molecule. Examples of A--T to G--C transitions.

by altering the structure of a base, so that its pairing affinities are changed.

The Mutagenic Action of Base Analogues

Ways have been found to induce mutations chemically, based on the theory of base pair transitions. One of these ways is to cause the bases commonly found in DNA to be

replaced by structural analogues that have a higher probability of tautomerism. An example of such an analogue is
5-bromouracil (or 5BU) which, as can be seen from the
structural diagrams in Text Fig. 23, is very similar to thymine.

It is not surprising, therefore, that if bacteria incapable
of synthesizing thymine from simpler substances are obliged
to grow in a medium containing 5BU in place of thymine,
5BU is incorporated into the DNA molecules that are
synthesized. The incorporation of 5BU takes place at the
expense of thymine, so that 5BU occupies the positions

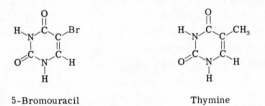

5-Bromouracil   Thymine

TEXT FIG. 23. Comparison of the structures of 5-bromouracil
and thymine.

normally occupied by thymine in the DNA molecule. An
interesting consequence of this replacement of thymine
by 5BU is mutagenesis. Bacteria containing 5BU in their
DNA undergo mutation with a much higher frequency than
occurs spontaneously. Similarly, if bacteriophage multiply
in bacteria growing in a medium containing 5BU, the bacteriophage DNA becomes labeled, so to speak, with 5BU,
and it undergoes mutation with a higher than spontaneous
frequency. The basis for the mutagenic action of 5BU seems
very straightforward. 5BU occurs in its tautomeric enol form
more often than thymine does. In its enol form, 5BU pairs
with guanine just as the enol form of thymine does. Consequently, when 5BU replaces thymine during DNA synthesis,
the probability of an A--T to G--C transition is increased
by the formation of an A--5BU intermediate. In this mutational route, the normal keto form of 5BU first replaces thy-

mine in a newly synthesized DNA molecule. However, another route also seems possible. Since the enol form of 5BU may occur in relative abundance in the pool of 5BU molecules serving as substrates for DNA synthesis, an enol tautomer of 5BU may be "mistakenly" confused for cytosine by a guanine base in a DNA strand that is in the process of specifying its complement. In this case, guanine pairs "illegitimately" with 5BU, and when the latter returns to its normal keto form, it will pair with adenine, rather than guanine, during DNA synthesis. We would have here a case of a G--C to A--T transition by way of a G--5BU (enol) intermediate. In this latter mutational route, mutation is effected immediately on the incorporation of 5BU, while in the former route, mutation takes place at some replication event after the incorporation of 5BU. The two hypothetical routes of mutation induced by 5BU are diagrammed in Text Fig. 24. Distinction between these two routes, one involving an A--T to G--C transition, the other a G--C to A--T transition, could be revealed by returning bacteria which have incorporated 5BU to a medium containing thymine. Any A--T to G--C transitions which have not yet occurred could still take place whenever a previously incorporated 5BU undergoes tautomerism. On the other hand, G--C to A--T transitions which have not yet occurred cannot occur in the absence of 5BU as a substrate. In other words, the first class of transitions is independent of a *continued* supply of 5BU, but not the second class of transitions. Experiments involving the removal of 5BU-labeled bacteria to a medium containing thymine have, in fact, shown that two classes of mutations are induced by 5BU, one dependent on continued growth in the presence of 5BU, and the other no longer requiring the presence of 5BU once incorporation of the analogue has occurred. Therefore, 5BU is believed to bring about mutations by the two types of base pair transitions described above.

One of the predictions of the Watson-Crick model appears to be fulfilled: procedures that are likely to promote base pair transitions are mutagenic. By the use of chemical mutagens, the other prediction concerning the formation of heteroduplexes may also be tested. Consider, for ex-

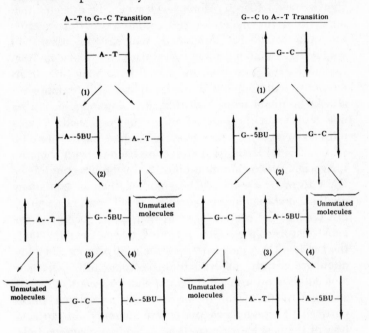

TEXT FIG. 24. Mutations by base pair transitions promoted by the incorporation of 5-bromouracil into DNA. 5BU° represents the enol form of 5BU.

The A--T to G--C transition takes place according to the following series of steps: (1) Incorporation of the keto form of 5BU; cells returned to medium containing thymine after this event. (2) Tautomerism of 5BU and abnormal pairing with G; this step could occur at any round of DNA replication. (3) Normal pairing of G with C, and continuation of mutation originated in step 2. (4) Return of tautomeric form of 5BU to its normal form and pairing with A.

The G--C to A--T transition takes place according to the following series of steps: (1) Incorporation of the enol form of 5BU; cells returned to medium containing thymine after this event. (2) Return of 5BU to its normal keto form and normal pairing with A; this step has a high probability of occurring immediately after incorporation. (3) and (4) Continuation of mutation originated in step 1.

ample, a molecule of DNA into one strand of which an enol form of 5BU has been incorporated. Such a molecule would be formally equivalent to the mutated molecule shown in Text Fig. 21. Moreover, it would be expected that one-half of the molecules descending from this mutated molecule would be unmutated, whereas the other half would be mutated, since every daughter molecule that derives its structure from the strand containing 5BU in its enol form will be mutated. Such mutational heteroduplexes should be found with great difficulty, however, since after one replication the heteroduplicity has vanished. A trick must be employed, therefore, to "catch" such heteroduplexes. The trick consists in infecting bacteria with bacteriophage DNA, allowing multiplication of the infecting phage DNA to occur for awhile in a normal thymine-containing medium, and then, just a few minutes before the first phage DNA molecules are enclosed in their protein coats to become mature phage, 5BU is added to the medium. Only the last few DNA molecules that are formed prior to maturation are thereby allowed to incorporate 5BU. Of these molecules, many can no longer replicate because they are arrested in the form of mature, nonmultiplying phage particles. These mature phage are liberated by artificial lysis of the host bacteria, and the individual phage particles are studied for the condition of their DNA molecules. This investigation is carried out by infecting a second group of host bacteria with single bacteriophage particles contained in the artificial lysate. Suffice it to say that some of these bacteriophage particles prove to produce a crop of progeny, half of which are mutant and half nonmutant, unlike ordinary mutant bacteriophage, which produce a uniform crop of mutant progeny. In this way, the existence of mutational heteroduplexes has been established. Their existence not only confirms the Watson-Crick double-stranded model of DNA, but also adds further evidence that each strand of the DNA molecule serves as a template in the formation of daughter molecules. If only one strand of the

DNA molecule were functional in replication, mutational heteroduplexes could never be detected, for they would always give rise to a uniform crop of progeny molecules, either mutant or nonmutant.

The Chemical Alteration of Bases *in Vitro*

The use of base analogues constitutes one way of elucidating the mechanism of mutation. Another way has been made possible by treating extracted nucleic acids directly with chemical mutagens. To incorporate base analogues into the structure of DNA, replication of the molecule is necessary. This requirement does not obtain when agents directly alter the structure of bases *in situ* in the DNA molecule. Such agents could act, therefore, on extracted DNA *in vitro*. Several *in vitro* mutagens are known, and one of the most powerful is nitrous acid (HNO_2). This substance has long been known to remove amino ($—NH_2$) groups from such substances as amino acids and amino-containing purines and pyrimidines. In particular, it is capable of deaminating cytosine to uracil (U) and adenine to hypoxanthine (H). Since uracil, like thymine, would tend to pair with adenine, and hypoxanthine, like guanine, would tend to pair with cytosine, nitrous acid can be expected to produce each of the following kinds of transitions: C--G to T--A (through the intermediate steps U--G → U--A) and A--T to G--C (through the intermediate steps H--T → H--C).

The *in vitro* mutagenic action of nitrous acid has been demonstrated in several kinds of experiments. The first was to treat the ribonucleic acid (RNA) of tobacco mosaic virus. As was explained in Chapter II, tobacco mosaic virus contains RNA instead of DNA, and the RNA is capable of transmitting genetic information. Tobacco leaves infected by untreated RNA extracted from mosaic virus produce mature virus particles of the same kind as caused the original infection. On treating mosaic virus RNA with nitrous acid, a large proportion of the treated molecules are shown to be mutated when they are allowed to infect tobacco leaves, because the mature virus particles to which they give rise contain genetically altered proteins. More will be said about these protein alterations in the next chapter; it suffices to indicate here that nitrous acid can mutate RNA directly, and it presumably does so by the kinds of base changes it is known to be capable of producing. Not only can the RNA of mosaic virus be mutated, but mature bacteriophage particles containing DNA can also be mutated by nitrous acid. After treatment with nitrous acid, extracellular bacteriophage may be allowed to infect host bacteria; when they do so, a very high proportion of the progeny are found to be mutant, as revealed by genetic alterations of various kinds. Since DNA is the principal component of the mature bacteriophage particle known to penetrate the host bacterium, the DNA molecule of the bacteriophage is believed to have undergone a genetic change. A final demonstration of the direct mutagenic action of nitrous acid on DNA is shown by the treatment of transforming DNA. In this case, DNA extracted from the wild-type strain of a transformable bacterial species is exposed to nitrous acid. The treated DNA is then found to produce a large number of mutant bacteria when it is allowed to infect competent wild-type bacteria.

Other *in vitro* mutagens are known. One is hydroxylamine (NH_2OH), which appears to react preferentially with hydroxymethylcytosine (HMC), which is found to occur in place of cytosine in some bacteriophages. It is believed to convert HMC to U and, hence, to produce an HMC--G to T--A transition. Another *in vitro* mutagen is ethyl methane sulfonate (EMS), which seems to cause the removal of purines from nucleotides by changing their structure and weakening the purine-deoxyribose bond. This action leaves the possibility for the "wrong" bases to fill the empty purine positions. Just as there are several *in vitro* mutagens, there are several base analogues capable of acting during *in vivo* synthesis of DNA. For example, 2-aminopurine (2AP) acts in a manner similar to 5BU. It is possible to compare the efficiencies and site specificities of these various mutagens. To do so, it is necessary to relate the frequency of induced mutations to the site of the mutation, as determined by recombination distances. One finds that, with any one of the mutagens, the likelihood of induced mutation is not randomly distributed along the DNA molecule. Rather, there is a clustering of mutations at certain sites, or "hot spots." On comparing the distributions of hot spots obtained with the different mutagens, two striking observations are made. One observes that two different mutagens may cause mutations at the same site, but do so with different efficiencies. Moreover, the hot spots for the different mutagens are not identical. If we assume that the sites of mutation are the bases of single nucleotides, two conclusions follow. The first observation tells us that two mutagens may cause mutations at the same nucleotide position, albeit with different efficiencies. In view of this conclusion, the second observation tells us that the nature of the base in a particular nucleotide cannot alone determine the probability of mutation at that site. In some way, the neighborhood of the nucleotide in question, perhaps the sequence of nucleotides in which the nucleotide happens to reside, affects the mutability of that nucleotide.

Mutations by the Deletion or Addition of Nucleotides to the DNA Molecule

Not all mutations can be simply explained as due to base pair transitions. A commonly detected form of mutation, arising either spontaneously or induced by some mutagens, is the so-called *multi-site mutation*. This type of mutation extends over a segment of the DNA molecule large enough to include several mutable sites. Moreover, multi-site mutations vary in extent, some being relatively large, others small. The length of the affected segment in such a mutation is revealed by recombination analysis. Imagine several mutations belonging to the same functional cistron or gene. Some of these may be shown to occur at sites capable of

undergoing recombination; such mutations cannot, therefore, occur at the same site. If two mutations of independent
origin fail to recombine with each other, it cannot, therefore,
be excluded that they occurred at the same site. The class of
multi-site mutations fail, however, to recombine with two
or more mutations that are themselves capable of recombining with each other. A diagram illustrating four multi-site
mutations of different size is given in Text Fig. 25.

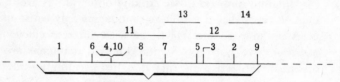

Region A of the DNA Molecule

TEXT FIG. 25. Multi-site mutations. Mutations in region A of
the DNA molecule produce a change in the same function. Sites
numbered 1 to 9 are capable of undergoing mutation and can be
recombined with each other; distances between the sites are based
on the relative frequency of recombination. Mutations 4 and 10 fail
to recombine with each other. Mutations 11, 12, 13, and 14 are multi-
site mutations of different length:

	Fails to recombine with mutations at sites	Does recombine with mutations at sites
Mutation 11	6, 4 (10), 8, 7	1, 5, 3, 2, 9
Mutation 12	5, 3, 2	1, 6, 4 (10), 8, 7, 9
Mutation 13	7, 5	1, 6, 4 (10), 8, 3, 2, 9
Mutation 14	2, 9	1, 6, 4 (10), 8, 7, 5, 3

Most of the multi-site mutations are very stable and have
not been known to revert to the original unmutated condition. A stable multi-site mutation can be understood most
simply as due to a deletion of the sequence of mutable sites
with which it fails to recombine. A deletion would obviously
be extremely difficult to reverse. It is not known how such
stable multi-site mutations arise, but, conceivably, breaks
at two points of the same strand in the DNA molecule could
result in a loss of the interstitial region during DNA un-

winding, with concomitant nucleotide-to-nucleotide joining of the distal sections.

Proflavine, an acridine dye, is a mutagen that seems to be capable of causing single nucleotide losses, as well as single nucleotide gains. Proflavine binds firmly to extracted DNA, and the proflavine-DNA complexes have been examined by a variety of physical and chemical techniques. The evidence suggests that proflavine reacts with DNA by intercalating between base pairs in the DNA chain. By the use of structural models, it is possible to conceive how DNA containing intercalated proflavine might suffer nucleotide additions or losses. The important evidence bearing on the mode of action of proflavine comes, however, from genetic studies. Proflavine is an effective mutagen *in vivo*. Unlike the large multi-site mutations that arise spontaneously, however, proflavine-induced mutations are restored to the wild-type condition rather easily. Such restorations of the wild-type condition arise spontaneously in proflavine-induced mutants. The wild-type restoration proves, however, not to be due to a true reversal of the mutation in the sense that the original wild-type configuration of the genetic material is restored. Rather, the restorations of the wild-type phenotype are due to compensatory *secondary* mutations at sites very closely linked to the original mutation. An example will be helpful in understanding how these secondary mutations act to *suppress* the effects of the primary mutation. A useful system for studying the action of proflavine are the rII mutations occurring in bacteriophage T4. These mutations cause the virus to be unable to multiply in the K12 strain of *E. coli* carrying the prophage λ (which is unrelated to T4). Such rII mutants of T4 are still capable of multiplying in the B strain of *E. coli*. In effect, the rII mutation belongs to a class of bacteriophage mutations that alter the range of bacterial hosts in which infection can be successfully completed. For the sake of brevity, the *E. coli* strain in which the rII mutant cannot multiply will be called K; the strain in which it can multiply, B. Consider the case

of an rII mutation produced by the action of proflavine.
By recombination analysis, it is found to occur at a specific
site in a nest (or cistron) of sites capable of undergoing
spontaneous or induced mutation to affect the particular
function necessary for multiplication in K. This rII mutant
may be allowed to multiply in B until a large number of the
rII mutant virus is obtained. This large mutant population
may now be examined to determine whether any single
member has undergone spontaneous reversion to the wild-
type condition allowing growth in K. It suffices to spread
K bacteria on the surface of a solid medium and then expose the bacteria to a spray of the rII mutants; a bacterium
infected by a wild-type mutant will lyse and release more
wild-type phage, and the spread of lytic phage on the solid
medium can be easily detected as a zone of lysis, called a
plaque. Wild-type revertants can be isolated from the
plaque. A B bacterium can now be simultaneously infected
by a revertant and by the original wild-type T4 phage. If
the revertant were truly a wild-type phage in its genetic
constitution, nothing should issue from such a double infection but wild-type phage—that is, nothing but phage
capable of growing on both K and B. The results of the
double infection show, on the contrary, that mutant phage
as well as wild-type phage are released. Among the mutant
phage released are two genetic types; one corresponds to
mutants containing the original proflavine-induced mutation; the other contains a mutation that "maps," by recombination analysis, at a site different from, but close to, the
proflavine-induced mutation. Finally, the two mutant types
can be "crossed" by the procedure of double infection just
described. The result is a reconstitution of the wild-type
revertant, a bacteriophage capable of growing on both K
and B, but possessing two closely linked rII mutations.

This experiment established that two mutations occurring
at sites very close to each other in the genetic material may
individually affect the same genetic function in similar
ways and yet *together* compensate for each other to produce

a nonmutant phenotype. This finding has been of extraordinary value in advancing our knowledge of how genes control specific phenotypic functions, and we shall return to this matter in the next chapter. For the moment, we need to consider the bearing of the finding on the question of proflavine's action. Let us call the original proflavine-induced mutation, O. The intracistronic suppressors that may arise spontaneously to compensate for the effects of O are many; they may map at somewhat different sites, but they are all closely linked; let us call all of them suppressors of type 1, or $supp_1$. Bacteriophage containing $supp_1$ mutations without O can be isolated, of course, and they have an rII mutant phenotype. One can look for wild-type revertants in the $supp_1$ bacteriophages. Such revertants are readily obtained, and they prove to contain, in addition to the $supp_1$ mutation, secondary compensatory mutations. Let us call the latter $supp_2$ mutations, since they are, in effect, the suppressors of suppressors of type 1. Similarly, bacteriophages containing only the $supp_2$ mutation can be isolated and then examined for wild-type reversions. In this manner, the suppressors of the suppressors of suppressors of type 1 are obtained; let us refer to these as $supp_3$ mutations. A big group of $supp_1$, $supp_2$, and $supp_3$ mutations has been accumulated, there being many different, independent isolations of $supp_1$ mutations, or of $supp_2$ mutations, or of $supp_3$ mutations. Members of any one of these classes of mutations are not identical because they do not map at exactly the same site. It is now possible to make various crosses involving different pairs of these mutations. Moreover, specific results are to be expected if certain assumptions are made about the nature of these mutations. If we assume, for example, that the original proflavine-induced mutation, O, is the result of a nucleotide loss, the $supp_1$ mutations might be expected to be compensatory nucleotide gains near, but not at the same site of the original loss. Conversely, if O were due to a nucleotide gain, a $supp_1$ mutation could be pictured as a compensatory nucleotide loss. According to this thinking, no two $supp_1$ mutations could recombine to produce a wild-type phenotype, nor could two $supp_2$ mutations or two $supp_3$ mutations, nor could any $supp_1 \times supp_3$ combination or any $O \times supp_2$ combination, any of which would by hypothesis bring together two nucleotide losses or two nucleotide gains. On the other hand, some as yet untested $supp_1 \times supp_2$ combinations, or an $O \times supp_3$ combination, could conceivably bring about a wild-type phenotype, since these combinations could bring together a nucleotide loss with a compensatory nucleotide gain. The results obtained from the various possible crosses are, for the most part, in accord with these predictions. The exceptional situations involve only some $supp_1 \times supp_2$ and some $O \times supp_3$ crosses from which wild-type phenotypes are not obtainable. In no case, however, was a wild-type phenotype produced when the hypothesis of nucleotide loss or gain did not predict it. The exceptions do have a theoretical explanation, which we cannot discuss here, except to say that this explanation has been tested experimentally and confirmed.

Although the genetic evidence supports the hypothesis that proflavine acts by introducing nucleotide losses or nucleotide gains into the DNA molecule, there is as yet no direct physical or chemical evidence. Perhaps no such direct evidence will be possible until techniques are developed for studying the nucleotide sequences of nucleic acids in their entirety. It is certainly safe to say, however, that proflavine acts mutagenically in a manner different from that of base analogues like 5BU or base mutagens like HNO_2. In the first place, intracistronic suppressors do not usually arise to revert HNO_2- or 5BU-induced mutations. Secondly, 5BU or 2AP fail to revert proflavine-induced mutations, although they can revert a very large fraction of mutations originally induced by 5BU, 2AP, HNO_2, or EMS. This finding is understandable if 5BU or 2AP causes base pair transitions, but does not cause significant numbers of nucleotide losses or gains. Interestingly enough, a majority of the spontaneous mutations that are capable of reversion (and hence are not multi-site deletions) cannot be reverted by

5BU or 2AP. Are these spontaneous mutations also due to small, possibly single nucleotide losses or gains, as in the case of proflavine-induced mutations? If so, they should be revertible with proflavine. While the answer is not yet known, it is obviously possible to obtain. This question has been raised here as an illustration of the value of the kind of theoretical considerations described in this chapter. The theory, rather than being idle speculation, directs geneticists —as good theory should—to the asking of specific, performable experiments and, thus, to the eventual expansion of our sphere of knowledge.

Recombination at the Molecular Level

Our theory tells us that the primary genetic material of organisms is DNA and that DNA is capable of mutation in a variety of ways, any one of which results in an altered sequence of nucleotides in the polymer. The word "primary" has been introduced, because we still have the function of RNA to account for. The case of RNA viruses, such as the tobacco mosaic virus, serves to remind us that RNA can carry genetic information, as well as DNA. The role of RNA will be left to the next chapter, however, as we continue here our investigation of how well theory accounts for the properties of DNA. In one respect, the Watson-Crick model of DNA structure has not been especially fruitful. It has failed to be of much value in understanding another important property of DNA, its ability to recombine. In the case of closely linked genes, or closely linked sites within the same gene, we know that genic separation, or site separation, can take place when homologous DNA molecules confront each other in the same cell. We know this when a DNA molecule that is genetically marked $+a$ is confronted with a homologous molecule marked $b+$ ($+$ representing the wild-type site of either mutation a or b). As a consequence of this confrontation, molecules carrying the genetic markers $++$, or ab, are produced. A recombination of the a and b sites has occurred. How does it take place?

Molecular geneticists are still pretty much in the dark

about this question. The Watson-Crick model does not indicate in any obvious way how recombination of DNA molecules might take place. It is possible to ask, nevertheless, whether the removal and replacement of a single nucleotide site can be effected by molecular recombination. To answer this question, three pieces of information are needed. The first is the total length of a molecule of DNA in terms of the number of nucleotide pairs present in the molecule. The second piece of relevant information is the length of the DNA molecule in terms of the total amount of genetic recombination that can occur along the length of the molecule. This information is usually expressed in some arbitrary units of recombination distance, as, for example, the percentage of recombinant progeny among the total number of progeny for each pair of mated parents. The parents and progeny examined are usually cells or organisms, not DNA molecules, which introduces an additional complication. In any case, making allowance for the complications, an estimate can be made from the first two pieces of information as to the number of nucleotide pairs involved in each arbitrary unit of recombination. The third piece of information, therefore, must be the smallest recombination distance between any two mutable sites of the DNA molecule. Knowing this, one can calculate the number of nucleotide pairs involved in this minimal recombination distance.

In practice, however, this information is not easy to get. It is not difficult, of course, to utilize a bacteriophage or bacterium, which appears to have only one DNA molecule carrying all the genes of the organism. Nor is the molecular weight of this DNA molecule difficult to determine. The molecular weight tells us how many nucleotide pairs exist in the molecule, since the average weight of a nucleotide pair is known. What is difficult to be sure of, however, is that one has determined the recombinational length of the DNA molecule, since this depends on having acquired mutations that are distributed rather uniformly along the whole length of the molecule. Obviously, it is not yet possible to arrange for the occurrence of mutations at specific, desired locations of the DNA molecule. Geneticists take the mutations they get. The mutations are then mapped, with the hope that they constitute a fair sample of the distribution of possible mutable sites. Another assumption one has to make in order to convert recombination distances into nucleotide pairs is uniformity of recombination along the length of the DNA molecule. If, for example, recombination were more frequent in one segment of the molecule than in another segment of identical length, our estimation of nucleotide pairs per recombination unit would be invalid. Finally, it is not possible to be sure that one has really detected the minimal recombination distance. For this purpose, one needs to study a very large number of mutations occurring in a small segment of the genetic material. This can be arranged when one selects for mutations affecting a specific function and the mutations prove, as they usually do, to be very closely linked. The smallest recombination distance one observes corresponds to the lowest value of recombination observed between a pair of mutations of this kind. Whether or not one has actually found this minimal distance is really a function of how many different intragenic mutations one can accumulate and study by recombination. In one case, that of rII mutations of bacteriophage T4, about a thousand such mutations have been examined. The smallest recombination distance that has been observed corresponds to a small fraction of the arbitrary unit of recombination. Supposing that the calculation of the number of nucleotide pairs in the T4 DNA molecule is accurate, and the estimation of the recombinational length of this molecule is a good one, it can be calculated that the smallest observed recombination distance corresponds to less than a nucleotide pair. It should be clear from this discussion that a number of assumptions, some of them not entirely verifiable, have been involved in this calculation, and so we should not put too much stress on the exact

number that has been calculated in this manner. Nevertheless, the effort to answer the question about the occurrence
of single nucleotide recombinations has had at least two
beneficial effects. The first of these is to make us realize the
extent of our ignorance, to make us formulate the assumptions that need to be validated. The second effect is the
reasonableness, if not certainty, of the conclusion that very
small segments of the DNA molecule can be recombined,
and that if a cistron or a gene could be exhaustively mutated
and mapped, the smallest recombination distance would be
that occupied by a single nucleotide pair.

The Mechanism of Molecular Recombination

Having satisfied ourselves that recombination of a very
small number of nucleotide pairs, possibly only a single one,
can take place, our efforts can be focused on a molecular
model to account for such a phenomenon. Two models have
been invoked to provide a molecular explanation of recombination. One model supposes that recombination is an aspect of DNA replication, indeed that it depends on DNA
replication. In this model, a molecule of DNA containing
the recombined sites is a newly synthesized molecule that
is the cooperative product of two molecules serving as alternative templates. For obvious reasons, this model has been
referred to as that of "copy-choice." It can be best described
by means of an illustrative diagram, which Text Fig. 26A
attempts to provide. In this diagram, two DNA molecules
are seen to confront each other, as they presumably must if
recombination is to occur. The two molecules are differently
labeled with respect to mutations, so that if recombination
occurs, the molecular products can be recognized. Consequently, one molecule is labeled $a+$ $b+$ $c+$ and the other
$a-$ $b-$ $c-$. Another aspect of the confrontation is that homologous sites line up so that they are side by side. Thus,
the $a+$ site of one molecule is next to the $a-$ site of the
other molecule, and so on. The homology of the confrontation is presumed to take place because of the efficiency and

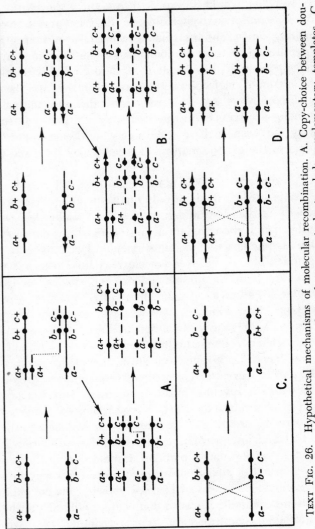

TEXT FIG. 26. Hypothetical mechanisms of molecular recombination. A. Copy-choice between double-stranded DNA templates. B. Copy-choice between single-stranded complementary templates. C. Breakage-reunion between double-stranded DNA. D. Breakage-reunion between single-stranded DNA.

accuracy of recombination. The mixing-up of genic sequences, which would be expected to occur if the confrontation were not exactly homologous, does not result from recombination to any appreciable extent. The next step is the production of the recombinant molecule. In the copy-choice model, a DNA molecule is synthesized first with one of the "parental" molecules serving as a template, and then, after the "copying" has proceeded for a distance, the nascent molecule switches to the other parental molecule for copying purposes. If the switch in copying occurs between the sites of the genetic markers, a recombinant molecule is produced.

In the copy-choice model of molecular recombination that has just been described, the alternative templates are assumed to be double-stranded, native DNA molecules. On the other hand, the template action believed to take place in DNA synthesis is that of single-stranded DNA. As will be discussed subsequently, it is not clear whether recombination occurs between double-stranded or single-stranded molecules. To allow for the possibility of recombination by copy-choice occurring between single, complementary strands that are genetically different, some additional assumptions have to be made, but they are not impossible to conceive. Text Fig. 26B gives an illustration of the assumed mechanism in this case. The parental, recombining strands are shown in heavy lines. First, a complete copy is made along one of the strands. Next, a copy is started along the other parental strand, and then copying is switched to the copy that had just previously been completed. In brief, it is necessary to postulate a parental strand and a newly synthesized strand *of similar polarity*, in order for a recombinant strand to be produced by copy-choice. This recombinant strand could either form a double helix with one of the two available complementary strands (parental or newly synthesized), or it could serve as a template for its own complement, with which it would then form a double helix. In the former case, one would have to imagine the existence of a *recombinational heteroduplex,* which might not be impossible to form and, in any case, would have the same transitory nature as a *mutational heteroduplex.* It would give rise to a parental molecule and a recombinant molecule in its next round of replication. However the synthesis by copy-choice of the recombinant molecules is postulated to occur, active synthesis of new DNA is required.

In contradistinction to the copy-choice model, another model of genetic recombination does not postulate DNA synthesis. This model, referred to as that of breakage-reunion, assumes that breaks occur along the length of the DNA molecule and that, when recombining DNA molecules confront each other, the breaks occur at homologous sites. Once breaks at homologous points are produced, recombination is achieved by the pieces of one broken molecule attaching to the pieces of the other broken molecule, as shown in Text Fig. 26C. Should the pieces of a broken molecule reunite with each other instead of with the pieces of the molecule it is confronting, as may happen, recombination of course does not occur. Again, it is possible to suppose that breakage-reunion takes place between two native, double-stranded DNA helices or between two strands, one from each molecule of the confronting pair. In the latter case, it would be necessary to postulate that breakage-reunion occurs between strands *of the same polarity,* as shown in Text Fig. 26D. The newly formed recombinant strands could serve as templates for the synthesis of their own complements, with which they could then enter into double-stranded helical configurations. On the other hand, it is conceivable that the newly formed recombinant strands could enter into helical configurations with the strands of the parental molecules which had not participated in breakage-reunion. If this latter possibility were in fact utilized, *recombinational heteroduplexes* would be formed, since each double helix would contain one parental strand and one recombinant strand. As mentioned previously, such recombinational heteroduplexes would, in fact, be short-lived, inasmuch as their first act of replication would resolve them into purely parental and purely recombinant molecules.

After setting forth the various possibilities by which molecular recombination may occur, it would be satisfying if experimental evidence were available to discard some of them. At the present time, the available evidence can be said to point suggestively in a certain direction, although a clear and definitive picture of recombination is not yet at hand. A decisive way to discriminate between the copy-choice and breakage-reunion models would be in determining the dependence of recombination on DNA synthesis. The copy-choice model postulates that recombination is a by-product of DNA replication when molecules in the process of being formed have alternative DNA structures from which to choose as templates. To test this notion, experiments with transformable species of bacteria have been helpful. It is possible to transform a bacterium already possessing a genetic mutation, a, with the DNA extracted from a bacterium bearing a different mutation, b. In some instances, mutation a, introduced by transformation, recombines with mutation b, resident in the host bacterium, with the result that a and b become linked on the same molecule. This is shown by the fact that, if DNA is extracted from the recombinant ab bacteria and used to transform a nonmutant recipient, the mutations a and b are integrated together into the recipient genome with very high frequency—with a frequency much higher than could be accounted for by random penetrations and integrations of the a and b mutations borne on separate molecules or molecular fragments. To determine whether DNA synthesis is necessary for the linkage of the a and b mutations when one is introduced into a cell already containing the other, transformation can be carried out under conditions in which cell growth and DNA synthesis is arrested. The recipient b bacteria can be treated with a DNA in a medium devoid of nutrients, or in a medium containing specific inhibitors of DNA synthesis. Several minutes after exposure of the recipient bacteria to the transforming DNA, the bacteria can be broken open and their DNA removed. With the DNA removed in this way from briefly exposed recipients, one can determine in a second round of transformation, using nonmutant bacteria as recipients, the amount of transforming DNA that entered the first round of recipients and the fraction of that amount in which the mutation a is linked with mutation b. Moreover, one can determine from the amount of transforming activity of the b marker, considered alone, how much DNA synthesis did take place in the first round of recipients during their brief exposure to a DNA. The results show that appreciable linkage of an introduced mutation with a resident mutation can occur during a period of time and under conditions in which there is no *substantial* synthesis of DNA. These experiments could be taken by themselves to exclude the possibility of a copy-choice mechanism operating in DNA recombination, if it were not for the fact that certain reservations have to be made. These reservations are due to the technical limitations of the procedure followed in the experiments. The methods employed are not so sensitive that they could detect less than a few percent increase in DNA. This limitation is crucial, because the frequency of recombination by transformation is not very high. Only a very few percent of the recipient bacteria come to possess a and b in a linked combination, and if only this small percent of the total population were actively synthesizing DNA, the net increase in DNA might escape detection. This objection is valid, however, only if one imagines that the bacteria in which recombination occurs are not a fair sample of the DNA-synthesizing activity of the population as a whole. Nevertheless, it cannot yet be excluded that recombination requires DNA synthesis. More sensitive methods for detecting DNA synthesis will surely be employed to settle the matter.

The case against the copy-choice mechanism receives strong support, however, from an entirely independent line of investigation. The question may be asked not whether copy-choice can be ruled out, but whether breakage-union can be ruled in. Is there any *positive* evidence for a breakage-reunion mechanism? Such evidence comes from studies of recombination in bacteriophage. In this case, it will be recalled, bacteria are infected with two bacteriophage particles that differ in respect to a number of genetic markers. Recombination occurring between the vegetatively multiplying DNA of the two genetic types is detected by the appearance, in the eventual host lysate, of mature bacteriophage with recombinant genes. To determine whether recombination entails the physical combination of parts of the two kinds of DNA molecules, the techniques of isotopic labeling can be utilized. Using this procedure, one of the two mutant phages that are used in the cross (in the double infection, that is) is labeled with heavy isotopes of carbon (C^{13}) and nitrogen (N^{15}). To accomplish this labeling, bacteriophage-infected bacteria are grown in a medium in which these isotopes predominate over the normal atomic forms (C^{12} and N^{14}, respectively). Bacteriophage thus labeled with these isotopes are recognized easily in a density gradient created by centrifugation, as described in Chapter III. The important point is that "heavy" bacteriophage are separable and hence identifiable from normal or "light" bacteriophage. Moreover, if a bacteriophage were created so that its DNA were partly heavy and partly light, it too could be detected, provided the heavy component were large enough. Two kinds of mixed DNA can be detected. One kind is the "hybrid" DNA which would result from semiconservative replication, namely, the kind in which one strand is heavy and the other strand is light. The other detectable kind of mixed DNA is one in which an entire section of the double helix is heavy. In summary, a cross is arranged between two differently mutant bacteriophages, one of which is also labeled with heavy isotopes. The yield of phages issuing from this cross is then placed in a density gradient, and separate fractions of the gradient are then analyzed for their contents. Control crosses are also carried out to determine the outcome of crosses in which all of the infecting bacteriophages are either labeled or unlabeled. In brief, the results of such crosses support the conclusion that bacteriophage DNA is replicated by a semiconservative mechanism, but that superimposed on the replication process is a mechanism that breaks whole, double-stranded DNA molecules into fragments. In other words, bacteriophage DNA was detected that possessed heavy isotopes along only part of its length. Such DNA was found only in the crosses in which isotopically labeled and unlabeled bacteriophages were used in double infections. Moreover, DNA possessing heavy isotopes along only part of its length was associated with genetic recombinants, more of this type of DNA being that of recombinants occurring at high frequency than of recombinants occurring at low frequency. In crosses in which all of the bacteriophages were either labeled or unlabeled, only the hybrid type of DNA produced by a semiconservative replication was found. These results, therefore, provide unequivocal evidence that DNA breakage accompanies recombination. Unfortunately, they do not demonstrate as unequivocally that a copying mechanism does not also enter into the process. The fragments produced by DNA breakage either could join appropriate fragments to form complete DNA molecules, or they could be completed by a process that copies the missing region from the homologous portion of a molecule of different parentage. If, however, breakage and reunion prevail rather than breakage and copying, the experimental data suggest further that recombination occurs between two double-stranded molecules. This suggestion derives from the finding of recombinant DNA molecules in which considerably more than half of the heavy parental DNA is present.

If the data of experimental investigations to date do not compel us to discard the copy-choice hypothesis of molecular recombination, they do indicate strongly that a process of breakage is involved. It is relevant, in this regard, to emphasize that the copy-choice and breakage-reunion mechanisms are not mutually exclusive, and that recombination therefore could involve both processes in the living organism. Finally, the experimental findings do not shed enough light on the question of whether double-stranded or single-stranded DNA molecules are engaged in the phenomenon of recombination. Nevertheless, the kinds of experiments described in this section point the way to further experimental attacks on the problem, for they indicate the restricted conditions under which recombination does occur and so prescribe the design of future experiments.

The Anomalies of Molecular Recombination

An understanding of molecular recombination is of interest not only in its own right, but also for what it could tell us about genetic recombination occurring at higher levels of biological organization. It is not certain that the recombination that occurs within chromosomes of higher organisms is simply the reflection of recombination occurring between the DNA's of which they are composed. Just as it is possible to imagine that more than one mechanism of molecular recombination may operate, it is conceivable that the recombination of DNA is but one aspect of chromosomal recombination. This question will receive fuller consideration in the final chapter. At the present time, we might consider whether recombination occurring at the molecular level exhibits unique features, properties that are not associated with chromosomal recombination. At least three such properties are worth mentioning here.

In classical studies of chromosomal recombination, it was regularly noted that the more distant two genes were to each other, the more frequent were multiple exchanges between their sites. In the terms of "crossing-over," geneticists observed that multiple cross-overs increased in probability as the recombining sites got further apart, and, conversely, the probability of multiple exchanges decreased as the recombining sites approached each other. However, the probability of multiple exchanges or cross-overs did not prove to be a simple function of distance. As the distances between the recombining sites got shorter, the frequency of two or more exchanges between those sites was less than the frequency expected on a purely random basis. If the two exchanges between selected sites took place independently of each other—that is, at random—the double exchange frequency should be simply the product of the frequencies of the single frequencies. In other words, if exchanges at two different sites always occurred independently of each other, the ratio of the observed to the expected frequency of double exchanges should be equal to one. On the contrary, the usual finding was that this ratio was less than 1, and that the magnitude of the discrepancy increased the closer the recombining sites. This phenomenon was referred to as *positive interference*, for it was believed that an exchange occurring at one site of the chromosome interfered with exchanges occurring at adjacent sites, possibly because of steric hindrance. The method by which positive interference was detected is shown in Text Fig. 27. A so-called three-factor cross is necessary to determine the frequency of exchanges between the distal markers and some intermediate marker, say between C and D and between D and E. When the resolution by recombination analysis became powerful enough, through the introduction of special selective techniques described in Chapter II, recombination could be carried out within the functional gene itself. In this way, the distance between distal markers could be reduced enormously, for recombination was effectively taking place between nearby nucleotides. When such intragenic, or fine-structural recombination was examined, the *sign* of interference was reversed. Instead of positive interference increasing in magnitude as the distances between recombining sites got shorter, the likelihood of multiple exchanges within a gene or between adjacent cistrons appeared to be enhanced. Indeed, the frequency of multiple exchanges was *greater* than that expected on the basis of independence of exchanges; the ratio of observed to expected frequency of multiple exchanges was greater than one. This is the situation occurring between sites *A*, *B*, and *C* in Text Fig. 27. In such a situation, one has to speak, if one speaks of inter-

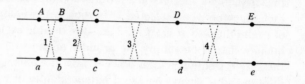

Let f_1, f_2, f_3, and f_4 represent the observed frequencies of exchange in the regions indicated.

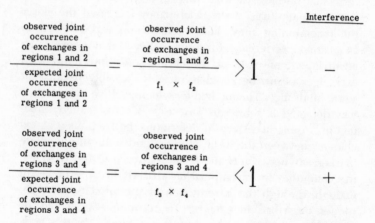

TEXT FIG. 27.　Negative and positive interference.

ference at all, of *negative interference*. A better way of describing this phenomenon is as an enhancement of recombination within very short distances of the genetic material.

How can one account for the *reversal of the sign of interference*? An easy way out is to suppose that recombination occurring within short distances of the genetic material, distances reckoned in nucleotides, is of a different nature than recombination occurring between long stretches of the genetic material. This view is by no means required by the data, but it is a distinct possibility. What is being suggested is that the chromosome of a higher plant or animal is not as simple as the single DNA molecule-chromosome of the bacterial nucleoid or of the bacteriophage particle. It may be a much more complex organization of materials than the DNA molecule, complicated as the latter has proven to be. The discovery of negative interference at least warns the geneticist that a too hasty extrapolation from the molecular to the cellular level, from the submicroscopic to the microscopic level of biological organization, is not warranted by the facts.

Another note of caution is introduced by the discovery of the role played in recombination by the "neighborhood," a role apparently analogous to the role it plays in mutation. In classical genetics, the frequency of recombination between any pair of genes was a constant, under specified experimental conditions. At least it was not influenced by changes in a gene near the pair of genes between which recombination was being examined. Without this constancy, it would not have been so easy to construct the genetic maps of chromosomes of higher plants and animals. For the most part, similar constancy also seems to prevail for the frequency of recombination between intragenic sites. Were this not so, fine-structural mapping of genes would not be feasible. Yet sufficient evidence is now accumulating that there are exceptions to the rule. The frequency of recombination between two sites within a gene is not always independent of the mutated state of a nearby site within the same gene. The influence of the nearby mutation has been called the "marker effect," and it is illustrated in Text Fig. 28. While only a few cases of it have been studied in detail, future investigations of recombination at the genic level are likely to throw more light on the problem. One fact is already clear. In situations where the marker effect is prominent, recombination distances between adjacent mutant sites are far from additive. Fortunately, however, the property of additivity can be divorced from the property of linearity. That is to say, the linear arrangement of mutant sites can be determined unequivocally without necessitating additivity of the recombination distances between those sites. One method of demonstrating an unequivocal linear order involves the use of overlapping multi-site mutations or deletions (see Text Fig. 25). With this method, sites can be ordered in a unidimensional array on the basis of their being included (or not included) in "deletions" covering

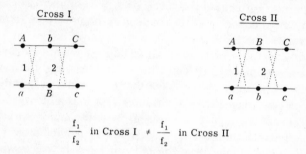

Cross I

Cross II

$$\frac{f_1}{f_2} \text{ in Cross I} \ne \frac{f_1}{f_2} \text{ in Cross II}$$

TEXT FIG. 28. Example of the "marker effect." Frequencies of exchange in regions 1 and 2 are represented, respectively, by f_1 and f_2.

different segments of the genetic map. (Thus, deletion mapping can determine the following order of sites in Text Fig. 25: 8, 7, 5, 3, 2, and 9.)

A third anomalous feature of recombination of sites within genes is the production of nonreciprocal structures. With such organisms as the mold *Neurospora*, in which the four products of meiosis are segregated into an ordered tetrad of ascospores, the individual ascospores can be dissected out of the ascus in which they are contained, and subsequent analysis of the ascospores reveals the genetic constitution of each product of a given meiosis. Analysis of this kind has been called "tetrad analysis." In general, when one is dealing with different genes linked to the same chromosome, tetrad analysis reveals two important results of the meiotic process in which intergenic recombination occurs: The two chromosomes containing the parental combinations of genes are always present in a given tetrad; the remaining two recombinant chromosomes are reciprocal products. Thus, if the two parental combinations of genes are $+a$ and $b+$, the two recombinant products in the tetrad are $++$ and ab. When, however, one is dealing with different sites within the same gene, the feature of reciprocal recombination is not always observed. Thus, if a and b are two sites within the same gene, and the parental combinations of sites are $+a$ and $b+$, the following kinds of tetrads are among those recovered: $+a$, $+a$, $++$, and $b+$; or $+a$, ab, ab, and $b+$. The occurrence of nonreciprocal recombination (sometimes called "gene conversion") is readily explained on the basis of a copy-choice model of recombination and, indeed, for a long time has remained the main support of the copy-choice hypothesis. Comparison of Text Figs. 26A and 26B with Text Figs. 26C and 26D will reveal that a choice between two alternative templates can often result in nonreciprocal products, while a breakage-reunion model, without additional modifications or assumptions, cannot account for nonreciprocal recombination. The difficulty of explaining nonreciprocal recombination by a breakage-reunion model is an additional reason, at the present time, for postponing the definitive relinquishment of the copy-choice hypothesis.

Cloudy as the picture appears now, further investigations of negative interference, the marker effect, and nonreciprocal recombination may be expected to contribute importantly to our understanding of the process of molecular recombination. To account for all of the data, some amalgamation of the breakage-union and copy-choice models may prove necessary.

The Molecular Model of Mutation and Recombination: a Summary

Disturbing and challenging as the new discoveries of mutation and recombination at the molecular level may be, they are extremely encouraging in one important respect.

They have given molecular geneticists a great deal of confidence in their theoretical approach. Not only has the willingness to create models and to test them been of extraordinary value in obtaining new and important information, but the particular model of DNA structure has withstood the rigorous scrutiny of experimentation. In no way have experimental findings failed to support the conception that DNA is a source of genetic information in the cell, that it has the double-stranded, helical structure proposed by Watson and Crick, that it replicates semiconservatively by the template activity of its complementary strands, that it undergoes mutation by changes in the nucleotide sequence of the strands, and that a DNA molecule recombines by a physical confrontation with another similar molecule, followed either by a physical exchange or by a cooperative contribution to a template product.

The questions remain as to how much further the DNA model can take us in understanding processes occurring at the molecular level within the cell and in understanding the phenomena observed at higher levels of biological organization. Our attention will be turned to these questions in the remaining chapters of this book.

CHAPTER V

THE HETEROCATALYTIC FUNCTION OF GENETIC MATERIAL

The structure of DNA has two functions. One of these is to permit its faithful reproduction with only rare errors. This is the replicative or autocatalytic function of DNA; its manner of achievement has been discussed in preceding chapters. The other function of DNA is to intervene in some particular biochemical step in the cell's metabolism, and the evidence already described suggests that DNA accomplishes this task by specifying the structure of a specific proteinaceous catalyst, or enzyme. This is the heterocatalytic function of DNA, and this chapter will be concerned with how this function is executed.

The Genetic Code

The building-blocks of DNA are deoxynucleotides, of which there are four common varieties, A, G, T, and C (the letters referring to the varieties containing the bases adenine, guanine, thymine, and cytosine, respectively). The building-blocks of proteins are amino acids, of which there are twenty common varieties. A list of the common amino acids and their structures is given in Table I. What can we mean by saying that the structure of some specific region of the DNA molecule determines the structure of

TABLE I

A List of the Common Amino Acids

Name	Structural Formula	Name	Structural Formula
Alanine	$CH_3-CH-COOH$; NH_2	Lysine	$H_2N-(CH_2)_4-CH-COOH$; NH_2
Arginine	$NH_2-C-NH-(CH_2)_3-CH-COOH$; $\parallel NH$; NH_2	Methionine	$CH_3-S-CH_2-CH_2-CH-COOH$; NH_2
Asparagine	$H_2N-C-CH_2-CH-COOH$; $=O$; NH_2	Phenylalanine	$\langle benzene \rangle-CH_2-CH-COOH$; NH_2
Aspartic acid	$HOOC-CH_2-CH-COOH$; NH_2	Proline	ring $\displaystyle \binom{N}{H}-COOH$
Cysteine	$HS-CH_2-CH-COOH$; NH_2	Serine	$CH_2-CH-COOH$; $OH \quad NH_2$
Glutamic acid	$HOOC-(CH_2)_2-CH-COOH$; NH_2	Threonine	$CH_3-CH-CH-COOH$; $OH \quad NH_2$
Glutamine	$H_2N-CO-(CH_2)_2-CH-COOH$; NH_2	Tryptophan	$\langle indole \rangle-CH_2-CH-COOH$; NH_2
Glycine	CH_2-COOH ; NH_2	Tyrosine	$HO-\langle benzene \rangle-CH_2-CH-COOH$; NH_2
Histidine	$HC{=}C-CH_2-CH-COOH$; $N \quad NH$; $\diagdown C \diagup$; H ; NH_2	Valine	$CH_3-CH-CH-COOH$; $CH_3 \quad NH_2$
Isoleucine	$CH_3-CH_2-CH-CH-COOH$; $CH_3 \quad NH_2$		
Leucine	$CH_3-CH-CH_2-CH-COOH$; CH_3 ; NH_2		

some particular protein? The structure of any region of the double-stranded DNA molecule is, we believe, determined by its particular sequence of paired nucleotides. The structure of a protein has several aspects, as biochemists have shown. First of all, there is its *primary* structure, which is given by its particular sequence of amino acids. Then there is the *secondary* structure of the protein, which is its manner of regular coiling in space, owing to the kind of chemical bonds between adjacent amino acids. There is also the *tertiary* structure, which is the peculiar folding of the protein molecule as a result of linkages between reactive groups sticking out of amino acids sufficiently close to each other in the molecule. Such reactive groups are the sulfhydryl (—SH) groups of methionine and cysteine, the hydroxyl (—OH) groups of serine, threonine, and tyrosine, and the secondary amino (—NH$_2$) or carboxyl (—COOH) groups not involved in the peptide linkage of the linear protein "backbone," occurring in such amino acids as arginine, asparagine, aspartic acid, glutamic acid, glutamine, and lysine. The interactions between these reactive groups, as well as certain other forces, account for the folding characteristic of specific proteins. Finally, there is the *quaternary* structure of certain proteins which are composed of polypeptide subunits; the quaternary structure relates to the manner in which these subunits are connected to each other. Thus, the functional protein of the cell has a three-dimentional architecture, and its arrangement in space has a great deal to do with its ability to combine with the substrate of the reaction it catalyzes as well as with other substances. More will be said about the quaternary structure of proteins further on; for the present, it will suffice to say that the secondary and tertiary structures of polypeptide chains appear to be dependent upon the primary structure, that is, the specific sequence of amino acids in the polypeptide. Consequently, the genetic determination of a protein's structure can be conceived as the specification of the sequence of amino acids in the polypeptide subunits.

In some way, therefore, the sequence of nucleotides in a certain region of the DNA molecule determines the sequence of amino acids in a particular polypeptide chain (assuming, as the evidence warrants, that different regions, or genes, specify the structures of different polypeptides). Using the idiom of communication, the primary structure of a polypeptide is said to be a translation, into the language of amino acids, of a DNA region, which is in the language of nucleotides. How is the process of translation accomplished? Combinations of nucleotides must be a *code* for amino acids. Obviously a single nucleotide could not code for a given amino acid, since the number of common amino acids (20) is in excess of the number of different nucleotides commonly found in DNA (4). Similarly, pairs of nucleotides would be inadequate as coding elements, or *codons*, since the maximum number of codons would be sixteen (4^2), which is still insufficient to code for all of the amino acids known to be present in the polypeptides of the cell. Triplets of nucleotides serving as codons would allow for sixty-four (4^3) possible combinations of nucleotides. Such a number would be in excess of that required, but one might imagine that certain nucleotide triplets represent "nonsense" (no coding function) or "special sense" (a function other than amino acid coding, such as interruptions between genes, necessary to the decoding machinery). It is equally possible to imagine that more than one codon specifies the same amino acid, so as to provide a certain amount of redundancy in the code. In coding parlance, identical translation from different codons is referred to as *degeneracy*. As will be mentioned later, there is evidence that the genetic code is, in fact, degenerate.

Another problem arises at this point. Are both strands or only a single strand of the DNA molecule read by the translating machinery? Put another way, is the code for the specification of a polypeptide's primary structure contained in the double-stranded DNA molecule, or in only one or both of the separated complementary strands? Experimental evidence on this question has only recently become available, and it appears that only one of the strands is actually translated. Indeed, from theoretical considerations, it is obvious that redundancy would be unavoidable if each of the two complementary strands were read by the translating machinery. In that case, —C—A—T— would have to have the same meaning as the complementary triplet —G—T—A—. While such redundancy would not be fatal, we shall overlook this possibility so long as current biochemical evidence suggests that a unique strand of the DNA molecule serves as the active template in translation. Of course, it is also abundantly clear that *both* strands of the DNA molecule serve as active templates in the *replication* of DNA, which is distinct from translation, at least in result.

The DNA in bacteria seems to exist as one continuous piece, and yet a very large number (probably thousands) of different polypeptide chains are specified under the influence of this one piece of DNA. How are the various messages, corresponding to the various polypeptides, read without confusion, so that a part of the message for polypeptide X is not added on to all or part of the message for polypeptide Y? At the present time, we may imagine certain types of nucleotide sequences as serving uniquely as message-separators, as the indicators of where one gene ends and another begins. But how about the region within the gene itself? Are there separators between the codons that specify individual amino acids in the polypeptide eventually formed? If, on the contrary, the gene is read in one continuous stretch without special nucleotide sequences serving as separators of amino acid coding units, one may ask whether the code is overlapping. In an overlapping code, the second nucleotide of one triplet would also be the first nucleotide of another triplet and the third nucleotide of still another triplet. The difference between an overlapping and a nonoverlapping triplet code is shown in Text Fig. 29. The evidence against an overlapping triplet code is strong. In the discussion to follow about the consequences of mutation on the amino acid composition of polypeptides, it will be shown that a single mutation in a gene is generally accompanied by a change in a single amino acid in the polypeptide specified by the gene. This finding has been observed in several cases of mutations affecting the primary structure of mammalian hemoglobin, of bacterial tryptophan synthetase, and of tobacco mosaic virus protein. The overlapping code would predict the contrary, that a change in a single nucleotide would usually

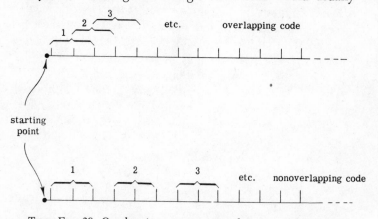

TEXT FIG. 29. Overlapping versus nonoverlapping triplet codes.

lead to a change of three amino acids in the specified polypeptide. Since this result is not observed, the genetic code appears to be of the nonoverlapping type.

The investigations of proflavine-induced mutations in bacteriophage have clarified some of the remaining questions. As will be recalled from the previous chapter, proflavine appears to act by adding or deleting nucleotides from the DNA molecule. Such mutations are often suppressed by secondary mutations that arise close to the site of the original nucleotide addition or deletion. The suppressive mutations are readily explained as compensatory deletions or additions (a deletion if the original mutation was an addition, an addition if the original mutation was a

deletion). Assuming that proflavine usually deletes or
adds a *single* nucleotide, the compensatory suppression is
also the addition or deletion of a single nucleotide. The concept of the genetic code provides a basis for understanding
the compensatory action of the suppressive deletions or
additions. On the first line of Text Fig. 30A is shown a
hypothetical sequence of nucleotide triplets, which, for the
sake of simplicity, are indicated as identical. Imagine that
this sequence is read from the left-hand end, represented
by a bar. The sequence is read, therefore, as a series of CAT
triplets. (Since CAT would code for a specific amino acid
in the protein formed under the direction of this nucleotide
sequence, the left-hand end of this hypothetical protein
would consist of a series of identical amino acids. While this
is an unlikely possibility, let us go along with this proposi-
tion, as it permits us to visualize easily the consequences of
deletion and of a compensatory addition.) Let us imagine
that a nucleotide is caused to be deleted at the site indicated
by the arrow with the accompanying minus sign. The result
would be the mutated sequence of triplets shown on the
second line. Thus, when the sequence is now read from the
left-hand bar towards the right, a new set of amino acids
is specified in the corresponding protein, starting with the
amino acid specified by the codon in which the deletion
occurred. We can easily imagine that such a protein will
be unlike the original produced by the "wild-type" nucleotide sequence and cause a mutant phenotype. If now a nucleotide is added at the point indicated by the arrow accompanied by a plus sign, a new sequence of triplets is
produced, as shown on the third line of the figure. The
new sequence is nearly wild-type, since most of the original
triplet arrangement is restored. In the case shown, only
three codons are still mutated. While these remaining mutated codons would presumably specify "incorrect" amino
acids, we can imagine that a very few incorrect amino
acids in an otherwise "correct" arrangement might still
preserve a sufficient amount of normal activity in the

specified protein and thus furnish a normal or nearly normal phenotype.

The addition of a nucleotide near a place where a nucleotide has been previously deleted can be imagined, there-

Original
"wild-type"
sequence —CAT· CAT· CAT· CAT· CAT· CAT· CAT· CAT· CAT· etc.
       - ↑

Mutated
sequence —CAT· CAC· ATC· ATC· ATC· ATC· ATC· ATC· ATC·· etc.
          + ↑

Suppressed
sequence —CAT· CAC· ATC· ATT· CAT· CAT· CAT· CAT· CAT· etc.
        ⎵‾‾‾‾‾‾‾‾‾‾‾‾⏜

         persisting
         mutated
         sequence

TEXT FIG. 30A. The suppression of a nucleotide deletion by an addition nearby.

Original
"wild-type"
sequence —CAT· CAT· CAT· CAT· CAT· CAT· CAT· CAT· etc.
       - ↑

Mutated
sequence
caused
by first
deletion   —CAT· CAC· ATC· ATC· ATC· ATC· ATC· ATC· etc.
               - ↑

Mutated
sequence
remaining
after second
deletion   —CAT· CAC· ATA· TCA· TCA· TCA· TCA· TCA· etc.
                  - ↑

Nearly normal
sequence after
third
deletion   —CAT· CAC· ATA· CAT· CAT· CAT· CAT· CAT· etc.
        ⎵‾‾‾‾‾‾‾‾‾‾‾‾⏜

         persisting
         mutated
         sequence

TEXT FIG. 30B. The restoration of a nearly wild-type gene by three successive deletions.

fore, to overcome the effects of the latter. Similarly, a nucleotide deletion can be imagined to reverse the effect of a prior nucleotide addition nearby. In this way, the known suppressive effects of proflavine-induced mutations can be accounted for, since proflavine is believed to bring about the addition or deletion of nucleotides. An important prediction can now be made about the nature of the genetic code. Assuming that proflavine adds or deletes *single* nucleotides, we should predict that a combination of three deletions, or of three additions, could allow a nearly normal protein to be formed. Text Fig. 30B shows how three successive deletions, occurring at nearby, but not identical sites, can result in a nucleotide sequence preserving most of the original pattern. Thanks to F. H. C. Crick and his collaborators, an experimental test was made of this prediction. It was found that no combination of two deletions, or two additions, or of two deletions plus one addition, or of two additions plus one deletion, ever produced a normal phenotype. On the other hand, several combinations of three deletions, or of three additions did give a normal or nearly normal phenotype. This is the result expected if the genetic code were a triplet code, that is, if the genetic information of DNA resided in the sequence of nucleotide triplets. Each triplet would be a codon, specifying an amino acid in the polypeptide chain formed under the direction of the gene. Moreover, according to this idea, the particular position of an amino acid in the polypeptide chain would correspond to the particular position occupied by the specifying codon within the gene.

While the results obtained by combining proflavine-induced mutations are consistent with the idea that the genetic code is based on a pattern of nucleotide triplets, an assumption underlying this consistency, it will be recalled, was that proflavine induced deletions or additions of single nucleotides. While this assumption seems likely, it is possible that proflavine generally causes the deletion, or addition, of several adjacent nucleotides at a time. The proflavine-induced deletion, or addition, could, therefore, be of a *block* of nucleotides. If such were the case, the codon would not be a triplet, but some multiple of a triplet, the multiple being the *average* number of nucleotides removed or added by proflavine in the mutational events it induces. Until evidence indicates the contrary, however, the model we will adopt is that of a triplet code, in the full awareness that the model may be subject to some modification in the future.

The Indirect Action of the Genetic Code: The Role of RNA

Accepting the view that the amino acid sequence of a polypeptide manufactured in the cell is ultimately traceable to the sequence of nucleotides in a particular region of the cell's DNA, we are still left with the question of how the specification is brought about. Is the polypeptide formed by the gene directly? For example, are the amino acids lined up on the gene, which acts as a template directing where the various amino acids are to go in the polypeptide that is formed? Such direct synthesis of the polypeptide on the gene template is not supported by the experimental evidence. A compelling piece of evidence is the localization of protein synthesis. In the cells of higher organisms, in which the cytoplasm is at some distance from the chromosomes inside the nucleus, proteins are synthesized in the cytoplasm, primarily on small particles, called ribosomes, attached to the endoplasmic reticulum (the internal, cytoplasmic membrane of the cell). The synthesis of proteins is, therefore, far removed from the DNA carried on the chromosomes. One has to suppose that the synthesis of proteins is only indirectly specified by the genic repertoire of the chromosomes.

What is the nature of the "messenger" that carries the information coded in the genes to the cytoplasmic sites where protein synthesis actually takes place? Fortunately, there is ample evidence to answer this question. The answer, moreover, tells us a great deal about the information-carrying capacity of ribonucleic acids, the type of nucleic acids to which we have not yet devoted much attention in this book. Since 1940, ribonucleic acid, or RNA, has been implicated in protein synthesis. This implication was derived from observations made independently by Jean Brachet in Belgium and Thorbjörn Caspersson in Sweden. These biologists noted that RNA is found in both the nuclei and in the cytoplasm of the cells of higher organisms, but that the amount of RNA in the cytoplasm is closely correlated with the rate of protein synthesis of the cell. Cells that are not actively synthesizing protein are relatively poor in cytoplasmic RNA, as compared to synthetically active cells, and when the rate of protein synthesis is increased, the amount of cytoplasmic RNA goes up markedly. The hypothesis was put forward that some RNA manufactured in the nucleus makes its way to the cytoplasm where it is involved in protein synthesis. Such RNA is a logical candidate for the messenger of the genes.

Since the role of RNA in protein synthesis was first suggested, a great deal of biochemical work has been done on this type of nucleic acid. An understanding of the way in which *messenger* RNA works had to await the unraveling of the different functions of what proved to be different kinds of RNA molecules. Cellular RNA is quite heterogeneous, and today we recognize three main kinds. Each kind belongs to the category of ribonucleic acids, because it consists of polynucleotidic chains in which the individual units are ribonucleotides. The ribonucleotides found in cells differ from the deoxyribonucleotides in two principal respects. The ribonucleotide, like the deoxyribonucleotide, consists of a purine or pyrimidine base linked to a 5-carbon sugar, which is in turn linked to a phosphate group. In the case of ribonucleotides, however, the sugar is ribose, instead of deoxyribose. Guanine and adenine are the common purines found in RNA, as in DNA. However, the common pyrimidines in RNA are cytosine and uracil, instead of the cytosine and thymine found in DNA. In other words, uracil appears to replace thymine in RNA. Nevertheless, it is easily conceivable that the sequence of adenine-, uracil-, guanine-, and cytosine-containing ribonucleotides in an RNA molecule could be specified by the sequence of deoxyribonucleotides in one of the strands of a DNA molecule. This specification could occur in a manner similar to that in which one strand of a DNA molecule specifies the structure of a complementary strand.

The three kinds of RNA are distinguished by their size and function. One kind is called *soluble* or *transfer* RNA — *soluble* because it is a small molecule, composed of 20 or 30 ribonucleotides, and hence relatively soluble in aqueous solutions, and *transfer* because it is involved in the transport of amino acids to the ribosomes where proteins are manufactured. There appears to be a different *transfer* RNA for each kind of amino acid found in proteins, so that there is a specific binding between a given *transfer* RNA molecule and a particular amino acid. This specific binding is mediated by an *activating enzyme* (the catalyst of reaction sequence I or II, page 36), which has the property of recognizing both the amino acid and *transfer* RNA. The *transfer* RNA-amino acid complex then attaches to a particular site on the ribosome, from which the *transfer* RNA molecule is released when the amino acid delivery has been effected. A given *transfer* RNA molecule may make many trips to the ribosomes. The ribosomes contain two other kinds of RNA molecule. Both are large molecules, in possessing high molecular weights and being composed of a very large number of ribonucleotides. However, these two kinds of high molecular weight RNA have distinct properties. One kind may be called the strictly *ribosomal* RNA, because it is a stable component of the ribosomes. During protein synthesis, this *ribosomal* RNA is not broken down and resynthesized. On the other hand, the other kind of high molecular weight RNA is less stable, and it undergoes breakdown during protein synthesis. There may be different degrees of instability or breakdown, depending on the specific messenger or the species of organism. In any case, this latter kind of RNA is believed to be the *messenger* RNA. It not only exhibits relative instability compared to *ribosomal* RNA, but it is readily released from ribosomes when the concentration of magnesium ions is lowered in the medium surrounding the ribosomes. Such treatment leaves the *ribosomal* RNA largely intact within the ribosomal particles. The *messenger* RNA fraction is very heterogeneous in size, unlike strictly ribosomal RNA, which is very homogeneous in size. Moreover, the proportions of the different ribonucleotides in *messenger* RNA reflect the proportions of the different deoxyribonucleotides in DNA. Thus, the relative proportions of adenine-, uracil-, guanine-, and cytosine-containing nucleotides in *messenger* RNA are very similar to the relative proportions, respectively, of the adenine-, thymine-, guanine-, and cytosine-containing nucleotides in the DNA of the cell. As has been noted previously, the deoxyribonucleotide composition of DNA varies widely from one species to another. Yet the ribonucleotide composition of the *messenger* RNA varies as does the deoxyribonucleotide composition of the species DNA, even though the ribonucleotide composition of strictly *ribosomal* RNA is very similar from one species to the next. The similarity in base composition of DNA and *messenger* RNA is one of the facts suggesting that *messenger* RNA is, in fact, produced by nuclear DNA acting as a template. In some way, *messenger* RNA is believed to make its way to the cytoplasm, where it becomes attached to ribosomal particles. The current working hypothesis in molecular genetics is that there are many different kinds of *messenger* RNA molecules corresponding to the different protein-specifying genes in the chromosomes. Each specific *messenger* is produced by a specific gene. Since the nucleotide sequence of a *messenger* RNA is presumably a *transcript* of the nucleotide sequence in a given gene, the messenger molecule carries the information for assembling amino acids in a specific arrangement. Attached to the ribosomes, the *messenger* RNA molecule is conceived to act as a template in its turn, by causing the different kinds of amino acids to align themselves along its length according to the sequence of nucleotide triplets, or codons. The small *transfer* RNA molecule, carrying a specific amino acid, is thought to recognize a specific codon. In this way, it delivers an amino acid to a particular place along the length of the *messenger* RNA template. With the various amino acids thus aligned, peptide bonds are formed between the amino acids, a polypeptide is created, and the *transfer* RNA's are released for further transporting activities. In this process, too, the *messenger* RNA molecule may have a high probability of destruction; that is, only a few polypeptide molecules may be produced for each *messenger* RNA molecule that is synthesized. At least, such is the case for *messenger* RNA molecules specifying certain proteins in bacteria.

Experimental Verification of the Messenger Model of Protein Synthesis

The model for protein synthesis that has just been outlined has two main features. First, it postulates that a particular kind of RNA, reflecting in its base composition that of the DNA, is produced by the chromosomes. Secondly, this *messenger* RNA is transported to the cytoplasm where, attached to ribosomes, it specifies the structure of polypeptides. In other words, DNA is *translated* into protein by first being *transcribed* into RNA. Biochemists have provided strong experimental support for each of these features of the model.

Biochemists try to understand the functioning of the cell, and of the organism of which the cell may be a part, by extracting and isolating particulate and molecular components of the cells. These components are then measured for various kinds of chemical activity, and the biochemist attempts to reconstruct their integrated functioning within the cell on the basis of their isolated activities. Sometimes such dissection of the cell's metabolic machinery is disappointing in the lack of light it throws on our understanding of the cell's economy. At other times, however, and this is especially true in the case we are about to explore, the biochemical methodology has resounding success.

In the first place, biochemists have isolated from cells a system composed of several constituents which is capable of producing RNA *in vitro*. The RNA synthesized by this system is of high molecular weight and is composed of the common four ribonucleotides (A, U, G, and C) which must be supplied to the system for synthesis to occur. The enzymatic constituent of the system, protein in nature, is called an RNA polymerase, and in order for it to catalyze the union of ribonucleotides, another component of the system must be present. This essential component is DNA, and only small amounts of DNA are required. DNA from sources different than those from which the polymerase was acquired may function in this system. The DNA appears to act as a template, for the proportions of the four ribonucleotides (A, U, G, and C) in the RNA synthesized by the system is determined by the proportions of the four deoxyribonucleotides in the DNA employed in the system. In the cells of higher organisms, this DNA-dependent, RNA-synthesizing system is found in the nuclei. Thus, the first requisite of the messenger model has been provided, namely, a nuclear machinery for synthesizing RNA as a transcript of DNA.

The other requisite of the model is a system associated with the ribosomes which can synthesize proteins according to the formula contained in an RNA code. Such a system has also been discovered by biochemists. The system contains ribosomes isolated from living cells, plus a number of other constituents. Amino acids bound to *transfer* RNA molecules are an essential part of the system. In addition to the RNA and protein known to be contained in ribosomes, another source of RNA is required for protein synthesis to occur. This source of RNA, under natural conditions, appears to be the unstable RNA, derived from the nucleus, which attaches to the ribosomes in a reversible manner according to magnesium ion concentration. By a wonderful stroke of good fortune, it was found that the natural source of *messenger* RNA can be replaced experimentally by an artificially synthesized RNA. What is particularly advantageous about the use of artificial RNA polymers is that they can be made to have specific nucleotide compositions. Thus, the first kind of synthetic RNA used in the *in vitro* protein-synthesizing system was one in which the ribonucleotides were all alike, in that the unique base was uracil. Such a —UUU— RNA was effective in promoting the synthesis of polypeptides. The unusual result was obtained, however, that the polypeptide thus synthesized contained only one kind of amino acid, phenylalanine. Indeed, when the —UUU— RNA is employed, the only amino acid that has to be presented to the protein-synthesizing system is phenylalanine, although protein synthesis is blocked unless all of the common amino acids are presented to the system when natural RNA is employed. Assuming a triplet code, it was concluded, in this way, that triplets of uracil code for phenylalanine.

The use of artificial messengers has been greatly extended and wonderfully exploited. Artificial RNA's have been produced in which two and even three different ribonucleotides are present (A+U, or U+G, or A+U+G, etc.). Moreover, the relative proportions of the different nucleotides could be varied. Thus, an RNA can be made containing 5 U for every A, or an RNA can be produced containing 1 U for every A. Knowing that the ribonucleotides are distributed at random, one can calculate the relative frequency within the RNA polymer of the various possible kinds of triplets (AUU, AAU, AAA, UUU, for example, in the A+U RNA). One then determines which amino acids are incorporated into proteins under the action of such an RNA, and one can also determine the *relative proportions* with which the different amino acids are incorporated. In this manner, it has been possible to discover that particular proportions of nucleotides in the RNA "messenger" cause particular proportions of specific amino acids to be incorporated. One also finds that the proportions of the various triplet combinations of nucleotides, calculated to be in the RNA messenger, correlate well with the proportions of amino acids known to be incorporated into protein under the influence of the messenger. Imagine, for example, an RNA polymer containing 25 UUU triplets for every 5 triplets containing one A and two U and for every triplet containing two A and one U. Imagine, moreover, that such an RNA causes the incorporation into polypeptide of 25 phenylalanine molecules and 5 tyrosine molecules for every asparagine molecule. One deduces tentatively that UUU codes for phenylalanine, that a triplet consisting of two U and one A codes for tyrosine, and a triplet consisting of two A and one U codes for asparagine.

Since the code that one deduces in this way is consistent with codes deduced from the use of various kinds of artificial RNA messengers, differing in their nucleotide composition, confidence is increased that the natural code for translating RNA into protein is being unraveled.

Extraordinary progress has been made along these lines. It would take us too far afield to discuss all of the significant findings made in this exciting field of biochemical research. Only two points will be made insofar as they relate to the nature of the genetic code. The first point is that the code appears to be degenerate. Two or more different triplets may, in some cases, code for the same amino acid. Yet the extent of degeneracy is not great. The other point is that the RNA of tobacco mosaic virus may serve as a messenger in the *in vitro* protein-synthesizing system. Therefore, it carries genetic information for manufacturing proteins. Presumably, in the tobacco cell infected with mosaic virus RNA, the latter is its own messenger for directing the synthesis of protein typical of the mosaic virus. Since it is possible to induce known kinds of changes in the RNA structure by specific chemical mutagens (see Chapter IV), one could look for changes in the amino acids of the mosaic virus protein as a consequence of a chemically-induced mutation in the viral RNA. These investigations were carried out, and the results lead to two important conclusions. First of all, as was mentioned earlier, the most frequent type of change in the viral protein molecule resulting from an RNA mutation was the replacement of a *single* amino acid by a different one. Rarely were two amino acids changed in the molecule, and when this happened, the two amino acids were not close to each other in the protein molecule. This evidence, of course, supports the idea that the code is not of the overlapping variety. The other important conclusion concerned the nature of the amino acid changes. Every amino acid change that was observed was consistent with the simple notion that a single ribonucleotide had been changed by mutation (A to G, for example, or C to U) in the RNA molecule. For example, one of the amino acid changes that was found in the viral protein following a nitrous acid-induced mutation in the viral RNA was the substitution of serine for proline. According to the picture of the RNA-protein code being established by biochemists, —CUC— codes for proline. A transition of C to U would produce the triplet —CUU—, which is, indeed, supposed to code for serine. Thus, a check of the consistency of the biochemically derived code with the observed amino acid alterations produced by mutation led to gratifyingly positive results. Mutations induced in bacterial DNA have also been produced which cause single amino acid substitutions in specific proteins. These amino acid changes could also be satisfactorily interpreted on the basis of our present knowledge of the code.

Colinearity of the Structural Gene with the Polypeptide It Determines

The concept that genes specify the structure of polypeptide chains through their sequences of nucleotides has, therefore, gained ascendancy in our thinking about the gene's heterocatalytic function. It must be added quickly, however, that this view has had to be modified only slightly. As will be discussed shortly, not all genes appear to act by specifying the structures of polypeptides. Some, in fact, do; when such genes are mutated, they cause amino acid substitutions in certain specific polypeptide chains. Such genes are called *structural genes.* There is another class of genes, to be described below, that regulate the transcription of structural genes, that determine, in other words, whether a given structural gene will function heterocatalytically or not. Such *regulator genes* are believed to control the transcription of structural genes through products the chemical nature of which is not known at the present time.

For the class of structural genes, however, the current model prescribes that for every codon in a structural gene there is an amino acid in a *corresponding* position in the polypeptide it specifies. Thus, to put it simply, triplets at the left-hand end of the gene should code for amino acids at the left-hand side of the polypeptide; triplets at the right-hand end of the gene code for amino acids at the right-hand end of the polypeptide; and triplets in the center of the gene code for amino acids in the middle of the polypeptide. The view is, therefore, of a colinearity between sites of triplets in the gene and sites of amino acids in the specified protein. To test the validity of this prediction of the model of gene action, one needs to be able to determine two things: (1) where a mutation has occurred in the gene, and (2) where an amino acid has been replaced by a different one in a polypeptide. The site of a mutation in the DNA molecule can be determined approximately by means of recombination tests. The order of mutant sites in a gene can be determined by recombination analysis, and the distances between these sites can be measured in terms of frequency of recombination. If recombination frequency were strictly proportional to the distance between mutated sites, it could be a reliable index of physical distance. Although we have doubts about the general validity of this rule at the level of the DNA molecule, recombination frequencies still represent our only present means of determining distances within the gene, unreliable as they may sometimes be. Although more difficult to determine, the site at which an amino acid has been altered can be determined more accurately. The specification of the exact site of an amino acid change is based on biochemical techniques too complicated to discuss in detail here. The techniques consist, in brief, of fragmenting the polypeptide into smaller peptides by means of enzymes that cleave polypeptides at the positions of specific amino acids, determining the amino acid composition of the fragments, and reconstructing a picture of the entire polypeptide's composition on the basis of a detailed, and often tedious analysis of the various fragments. The net result of such an analysis is knowledge of the exact sequence of amino acids in a polypeptide from one end of the chain to the other.

Having obtained knowledge of the amino acid sequence in the normal polypeptide structure, one may then determine the exact position at which an amino acid is replaced by a different one as a result of gene mutation. Finally, one asks how the positions of the amino acid replacements correlate with the positions within the gene where the mutations occurred. The results of such analyses, while few in number, have been extremely rewarding. The work of Charles Yanofsky and his colleagues at Stanford University needs particularly to be cited. Their work has proven beyond doubt that there is colinearity between amino acid sites in the enzyme tryptophan synthetase of the bacterium *Escherichia coli* and sites in the gene determining the structure of this enzyme. The sites at which mutations are induced in the gene are, in fact, found in this case to correspond in a linear fashion with the sites at which amino acid alterations are caused by the mutations.

With the establishment of the validity of the concept of colinearity, another prediction of the model of the gene's specification of protein structure has been verified, and our confidence in this model has been thereby increased.

The polypeptide subunit of the protein molecule does, indeed, appear to be a linear representation in a different language (that of amino acids) of a specific region of the DNA molecule.

Proteins as Aggregates and the Phenomenon of Complementation

At the beginning of this chapter, reference was made to the fact that proteins are often found to be compounded of polypeptide subunits. As more proteins are studied, an increasing number is found to possess a quaternary structure. The biological significance of this structure lies in the fact that the activity or function of the protein is a property of its aggregate nature.

An excellent example in point is the red protein, known as hemoglobin, found in the red blood cells of mammals. A molecule of normal hemoglobin consists of four polypeptide subunits, two identical α chains and two identical β chains. The function of hemoglobin is closely tied to the aggregation of the subunits; when separated into its constituent subunits, the properties are altered. It seems rather clear that two unlinked genes are responsible for the structure of the two different kinds of subunits in the hemoglobin molecule. One gene determines the specific sequence of amino acids in the α chain; the other gene determines the amino acid sequence in the β chain. A mutation in the "α gene" causes amino acid substitutions in the α chain, without affecting the amino acid composition of the β chain. The converse is true for the "β gene." Many such abnormal or mutant hemoglobins are known, especially in man. Indeed, the first demonstration that a gene mutation may result in the replacement of a single amino acid in a specific protein molecule was provided with the famous "sickle-cell" hemoglobin. Humans suffering from sickle-cell anemia possess an abnormal hemoglobin in their red blood cells, and it was subsequently shown by Vernon Ingram that a single amino acid had been replaced in the β chain of this hemoglobin. This single amino acid alteration is the result of a mutation in the "β gene."

Similarly, the bacterial enzyme tryptophan synthetase, which Yanofsky has shown to bear a colinear relation with its structural gene, is known to be composed of an A and a B polypeptide chain. The A and B chains alone have somewhat different catalytic properties, but when aggregated into the final enzyme structure, the aggregate has special catalytic properties of its own. So far only proteins with dissimilar subunits have been mentioned. Yet some proteins are also known to consist of two or more identical subunits in aggregation. Such proteins have, in fact, led to a verifiable explanation of the phenomenon of complementation between two different mutations affecting the same polypeptide.

In Chapter II the test of complementation was described as a criterion for assigning mutations to cistrons. If two mutations complement each other (that is, produce a wild-type phenotype) when occurring in a *cis* or *trans* configuration, they are said to belong to different cistrons. If they fail to complement in the *trans* condition, but complement in the *cis* condition (the wild-type homologue of these mutations also being in the *cis* condition), the two mutations are said to belong to the same cistron. At one time it was hoped that the cistron would correspond to the functional unit of the genetic material; that is, it was hoped that each cistron would be responsible for the production of a specific macromolecule in the cell. Continued investigation revealed, however, that certain mutations assignable to different cistrons by a complementation test nevertheless affected the same polypeptide chain. Thus, it was clear that cistrons, as defined by complementation criteria, did not correspond to specific functional units. The alternatives are available to redefine the cistron in terms of the specific macromolecular product it controls, or to adopt the term *gene* as the functional unit. The former alternative not only has the objectionable feature of changing definitions in midstream, but it also presupposes knowledge of the specific product made under the influence of the functional unit of the genetic material. Unfortunately, the latter is far from being the common situation; rather, we often know of mutant phenotypes before we know what specific macromolecules have been primarily affected by the mutation in question.

	Structure of Polypeptide or Dimer	Enzymatic Activity
Normal subunit	WWWWW	−
Normal dimer	WWWWW•WWWWW	+
Mutant 1 subunit	W✗WWWW	−
Mutant 1 dimer	W✗WWWW•W✗WWWW	−
Mutant 2 subunit	WWWW✗W	−
Mutant 2 dimer	WWWWW✗•WWWW✗W	−
Mixed mutant 1- mutant 2 dimer	W✗WWWW•WWWW✗W	nearly +

TEXT FIG. 31. Complementation by mixed aggregation of mutant polypeptides. The jagged line represents a sequence of amino acids in a polypeptide specified by a structural gene. The point where two such polypeptides join to form a dimer is indicated by a heavy dot. The position in the polypeptide where an amino acid substitution has been caused by a mutation is indicated by a cross.

The important observation remains, however, that mutations belonging to different cistrons may affect the same specific polypeptide. How can this happen? Let us suppose that the polypeptide which these mutations affect is a repeating subunit in some cellular protein having a particular catalytic function when in the aggregated state. The protein formed in a cell homozygous for one of the mutations can only consist of mutated subunits. Such a mutated aggregate may be inactive. However, in a cell heterozygous for two of these mutations, the two different kinds of mutated subunits are made, and a mixed mutant aggregate may be formed. In other words, one mutated subunit may associate with the other kind of mutated subunit, as well as with itself. If the mixed mutant aggregate has normal, or nearly normal, activity as a consequence of its special quaternary structure, the two mutations would, in effect, be complementing each other (see Text Fig. 31). Thus, two complementary mutations could conceivably affect the same polypeptide, albeit at different amino acid positions. As the reader may surmise, such an hypothesis would not have been presented here had there not been ample evidence of its correctness in at least a few cases. Actually, this explanation of what may be termed *intragenic complementation* has been verified in certain cases of genetically altered bacterial and mold enzymes. Possibly it may prove to be the general explanation of all complementations found to occur within the boundaries of a structural gene.

Intergenic Suppression

Since the early days of genetics, as pointed out in the first chapter, different genes have been known to interact in the molding of a particular phenotypic character. A special case of genic interaction is that of *suppression*. Usually it is manifested in the following way. A given gene undergoes mutation, which causes some phenotypic alteration. Subsequently, another gene, which may be linked or unlinked to the first one, also undergoes mutation, resulting in a restoration of the normal, wild-type character. The mutant form of the second gene is called a *suppressor* of the mutated allele of the first gene, from which it can be separated by recombination.

Suppression of the abnormal action of one gene by a different gene is not the same sort of thing as intragenic suppression, which has been discussed in connection with addition-deletion types of mutations and their bearing on the nature of the genetic code. The reader will recall that, when a nucleotide is deleted within a given gene, a mutated nucleotide sequence results; the mutated sequence can be reversed, at least partially, by the subsequent addition of a nucleotide at a point not too far distant from the site of the original deletion. In this way, a mutation may be suppressed by a second mutation at a different site within the same gene.

Intragenic suppression is, therefore, not too difficult to understand. But how about intergenic suppression? How can the action of a gene be overcome by a mutation that is far removed and occurs in a nucleotide sequence serving an entirely different function? Several cases of intergenic suppression have now been examined at the molecular level, and it turns out that there is no one, all-encompassing explanation. Let us consider, first of all, some of the least interesting situations. These are the situations in which a mutated structural gene produces a defective enzyme, or no enzyme at all, and the suppressor does nothing to change this condition; rather, the suppressor acts indirectly to restore the normal phenotype. In one case, for example, a mutant strain of *Neurospora* produces a tryptophan synthetase that is exceedingly sensitive to certain metallic ions normally present in the organism. Indeed, the enzyme is inactivated by these ions, and tryptophan synthesis is thereby blocked. When a suppressor mutation occurs in the mutant strain, tryptophan can again be synthesized. However, extracts of the suppressed mutant strain are found to contain a tryptophan synthetase that is just as sensitive to metallic ions as that of the unsuppressed mutant. The suppressor *in vivo* is, therefore, believed to act to keep the intracellular concentration of the inhibitory ions sufficiently low as to allow the mutant enzyme to work and restore tryptophan synthesis.

Still other modes of indirect suppression are known. For example, a suppressor mutation may bring into operation a secondary, alternative pathway for the synthesis of a particular metabolite, and in doing so may overcome the effect of a prior mutation effectively blocking the primary synthetic route.

Were such indirect modes the only ones known, there would be no difficulty in explaining intergenic suppression at the molecular level. However, there are cases in which the suppressor mutation acts to restore the normal, or nearly normal synthesis of the enzyme affected by the original mutation. How can we square such a finding with the notion of the uniqueness of genes—with the notion that each gene in the organism's genotype has a unique, specific action to play in the molecular economy? Is this notion incorrect, and does more than one gene specify the structure of a given polypeptide? Fortunately, we do not need to resort to such an idea of the redundancy of genes. We do need to invoke, however, the cytoplasmic system of soluble RNA's, activating enzymes and ribosomes as well as the genes that specify the structures of these entities. This cytoplasmic system, it will be recalled, is responsible for translating the genic message into a specific polypeptide. The soluble RNA's (sRNA's) transfer the amino acids from their activating enzymes to the sites on the ribosomes where the amino acids are joined together in the sequence dictated by the messenger RNA produced by the gene. In this peptide-synthesizing system the sRNA's are rather specific, as are the activating enzymes, since they recognize and react with specific amino acids. Thus, for each amino acid there is at least one and, in some cases, possibly several mutually recognizing sRNA-activating enzyme pairs. To what do these activating enzymes and sRNA's owe their specificity? It seems likely that genes determine their structure. Possibly the activating enzymes are specified indirectly by genes acting through messenger RNA's, similar to those controlling the structures of all other proteins. The sRNA's, however, may be produced directly by their controlling genes, in a manner similar to that of the formation of messenger RNA's.

There is no direct evidence bearing on the genic control of sRNA or activating enzymes. However, the genes responsible for the structures of these substances may be the very ones in which certain suppressor mutations occur—the suppressors that restore enzymes made defective, or absent, by previous gene mutations. Theoretically, these suppressors would work in the following manner. Suppose a structural gene mutation resulted in the specification of an incorrect amino acid at a certain position of a particular protein, and that this amino acid replacement resulted in insignificant catalytic activity. Such a gene mutation, sometimes referred to as "missense," would be due to an altered triplet. This altered triplet would be transcribed into an altered messenger. The mutant messenger triplet, in turn, would react with an sRNA different from the "normal" one, so as to cause an amino acid different from the "normal" one to be placed in the specified position in the protein. When the suppressor arises, however, a mutated sRNA (or activating enzyme) would be produced that transfers the "normal" amino acid to the position of the mutated triplet in the mutant messenger. Thus, for example, if UUU were a triplet in a given messenger, it would call for the insertion of phenylalanine at the corresponding position in the specified protein. If mutation caused the triplet to become CUU, serine would be inserted in place of phenylalanine. If, finally, the gene controlling a certain sRNA mutated and caused the sRNA to attach phenylalanine to a CUU triplet, the original mutation would, in effect, be reversed.

In a similar manner, one could imagine how a suppressor could overcome the absence of a particular polypeptide. Suppose our hypothetical structural gene underwent a mutation causing a triplet to be produced that is "meaningless" or "nonsense"—a triplet that specifies no amino acid at all; the result might easily be no production of the specified polypeptide. A mutation in an sRNA-specifying gene (affecting recognition of the messenger codon) could suppress this defect by causing an amino acid to be put back in the position where previously no amino acid could be placed. Indeed, it is a good deal simpler to imagine how "nonsense" mutations could be suppressed by this mechanism than "missense" mutations. In the case of "missense" mutations, it is difficult to conceive how proteins other than the defective one would be spared the effect of the mutated amino acid transferring system. If amino acid X, say, were the one substituted into the defective polypeptide as a consequence of the structural gene mutation, the suppressor would replace X by Y, the "normal" amino acid, not just in the mutated spot of the defective polypeptide, but in every position of every polypeptide where X is normally found. Thus, the activity of proteins in general would be jeopardized by such a suppressor mutation unless, of course, X were rarely located in activity-controlling positions of proteins. Another possibility might be that the damage done to proteins in general by the suppressor is small because it is not 100% efficient; in this case, the general protein damage would be outweighed by the advantage of producing at least some active molecules of the specific enzyme affected in the mutant organism. If this were so, the suppressed mutant would not be quite normal, and it might contain inactive as well as active molecules of the affected enzyme. Such cases are, in fact, often observed. The problem of general protein damage does not arise, of course, in the case of "nonsense" mutations, for here there is no jeopardy in permitting a "nonsense" triplet to be read as "sense."

The hypothesized mechanism of intergenic suppression by mutations in the amino acid transferring system is obviously rather delicate. There are only limited circumstances in which it could serve. The experimental evidence regarding the existence of such a mechanism is scanty, but suggests that it might operate in the case of certain mutations. Suppressors, however, might act in still other ways to restore the enzyme made deficient by a structural gene mutation. One possibility lies in the action of the ribosomes. Until recently, the ribosomes were thought of as being passive factories in which the important interactions between messenger and soluble RNA's took place. The ribosomes, however, are now known to be more intimately concerned with protein synthesis than had been previously conceived. The ribosomes extracted from bacteria sensitive to streptomycin can serve only poorly as protein-synthesizing factories in the presence of streptomycin. On the other hand, ribosomes extracted from streptomycin-resistant bacteria are found to be much more resistant to streptomycin, and they can carry out protein synthesis at concentrations of the antibiotic which inhibit protein synthesis by ribosomes from streptomycin-sensitive strains. Moreover, with streptomycin-sensitive ribosomes, but not with resistant ones, streptomycin has the unusual effect of causing the misreading of messenger RNA. Thus, for example, in the presence of streptomycin and streptomycin-sensitive ribosomes, UUU no longer codes for phenylalanine, but codes primarily for leucine, isoleucine, and serine. Therefore, the ribosomal structure itself is in some way implicated in the protein-synthesizing process. In ways not yet understood, the conformation of the ribosomal sites to which messenger RNA's attach plays an important part in the reading of the message. This being the case, mutations affecting the ribosomal structure itself may have a suppressor function. Thus, for example, the gene, or genes, controlling the ribosomal structure may undergo several kinds of mutation. One kind of mutation is observed in streptomycin-resistant bacteria; the ribosomal structure is so altered as to be protected from the misreading caused by the presence of streptomycin. Another kind is observed in streptomycin-dependent bacteria; here the ribosomal structure is presumably so altered as to require streptomycin for normal reading. Finally, another kind of mutation is possible. This is one in which the ribosomal structure is so altered as to "correct" into "sense" the "missense" or "nonsense" of a particular mutant messenger triplet. The latter type of mutation would, in effect, be a suppressor.

At the present time, the theoretical bases for intergenic

suppression are well in advance of experimental verification. But this situation may be rapidly changed by current investigations into the molecular changes accompanying intergenic suppression.

Regulator Genes

It is not likely, in any case, that all genes act by specifying the amino acid sequences of polypeptide chains. Of course, it is necessary to imagine a great many structural genes controlling the formation of the variety of messenger RNA molecules which, in turn, mediate the synthesis of the variety of polypeptides contained in the cell. But there must also be a genetic control of the variety of soluble RNA molecules that recognize the different species of amino acids to be transported to the protein-synthesizing ribosomes. It is also possible that the structural RNA of the ribosomes owes its compositional specificity to a particular group of genes.

The most convincing evidence, however, of a class of genes distinct from structural genes comes from the study of the mechanisms regulating enzyme synthesis in bacteria. For a long time it has been known that cells do not always synthesize the proteins they are genetically capable of producing. Sometimes a substance coming from the environment of the cell will induce the formation of an enzyme. The exogenous agent is called an *inducer;* very often it is the natural substrate of the enzyme it causes to be produced, and it yields energy when metabolized. In this way, enzyme synthesis appears to be responsive to the need of the cell: when the substrate of the enzyme appears, the enzyme is produced, and not before. On the other hand, sometimes the synthesis of an enzyme is repressed when the concentration of a specific substance exceeds a certain value. The *repressor* is very often an amino acid, which can be toxic to the cell when present in too large an amount, and the repressor shuts off the synthesis of just those enzymes which lead to the formation of this amino acid. Thus, again enzyme synthesis appears to be regulated in an adaptive way. In the case of repression, the synthesis of an enzyme is turned off when it could cause the overproduction of a metabolite toxic at high concentrations.

The induction and repression of enzyme synthesis are known also to be under genetic control. Mutations arising in specific genes may cause either the inductive or the repressive mechanism to disappear. For example, in a cell in which the synthesis of a certain enzyme is normally induced, a mutation may arise resulting in the continual (constitutive) synthesis of the enzyme, regardless of the presence or absence of the inducer. Similarly, the synthesis of an enzyme that is normally repressible may be relieved of the repressive control as a result of a gene mutation. The genes that are thus demonstrated to determine the conditions under which certain enzymes are synthesized are called *regulator genes*. They are distinct from the structural genes, which determine the composition of the enzymes in question. The regulator genes do not affect the structure of these enzymes, but specify the conditions under which the enzymes are produced. Thus, when the mutation from inducibility to noninducibility arises, there is no alteration in the structure of the enzyme that is thereafter constitutively synthesized.

François Jacob and Jacques Monod in France have conducted an elegant genetic and biochemical investigation of the regulator gene which controls the synthesis of an enzyme, β-galactosidase, in *Escherichia coli*. Utilizing the technique made possible by the phenomenon of sexduction, they could obtain bacterial cells that were diploid for the regions of the regulator and structural genes of β-galactosidase. They produced cells that were doubly heterozygous in the following way: one chromosome contained a mutated form of the structural gene for β-galactosidase and, in addition, the wild-type regulator gene for inducibility; the other chromosome contained the wild-type structural gene for β-galactosidase plus a mutated form of the regulator gene. Thus, the double heterozygote may be described symbolically as *lac— ind+/lac+ ind—*, where *lac—* refers to the mutant form of the wild-type (*lac*+) structural gene for β-galacto-sidase and *ind*— refers to the mutant form of the wild-type (*ind*+) regulator gene. A haploid bacterium that is *lac*— *ind*+ produces no active β-galactosidase, whether the inducing substrate (lactose or other β-galactosides) is present or absent. A haploid bacterium that is *lac*+ *ind*— produces an active β-galactosidase in either the presence or the absence of the inducer. The double heterozygote, *lac*— *ind*+/ *lac*+ *ind*—, was shown by Jacob and Monod to produce an active β-galactosidase only in the presence of the inducer, but not in its absence. This experiment established two facts: (1) the wild-type form of the regulator gene is dominant over the mutated form, and (2) the wild-type form of the regulator gene may act on the structural gene in *trans* configuration (that is, the structural gene may be affected by its regulator located on a different chromosome). To account for this finding, it was supposed that the wild-type form of the regulator produced a diffusible agent having a negative effect on the synthesis of β-galactosidase. It was imagined, moreover, that the negatively acting agent is prevented from having its effect when the inducer is present. The loss of the ability to produce this negatively acting agent accounts for the phenotype of non-inducibility in cells with the mutated regulator.

This ingenious model proposed by Jacob and Monod can, with slight modification, account for repressibility and its genetic control. In this case, the product of the regulator is conceived to be inactive until it combines with the repressor. At the present time, the chemical nature of the agent produced by the regulator gene is not known with certainty, but it may be a protein. If so, it would be interesting to know if it were synthesized by way of a messenger from the regulator gene, in a manner analogous to that of protein specification by messengers from structural genes. Moreover, it would be important to know how the regulator's agent affects the activity of certain structural genes. Careful experimentation has revealed that this agent probably acts by preventing the transcription of certain specific structural genes. It seems as though the messengers of these structural genes are not formed in the presence of the regulating agent. The activity of several different structural genes in bacteria has been found to be under the control of regulator genes acting in a manner similar to that described for the β-galactosidase-synthesizing system. In this regard, Jacob and Monod uncovered another interesting property of regulation. Often transcription of a *group* of linked structural genes is controlled by a single regulator gene. That is to say, messenger production by this group of structural genes is turned on or off in a coordinated way. Heterocatalytically, this group of structural genes behaves as a unit, and Jacob and Monod have proposed the term *operon* for such a coordinately regulated unit. A particular spot at one end of the operon, called the *operator,* is specifically sensitive to the action of the regulator's agent.

The feature of the operon that is of adaptive value to the cell is the biochemical relatedness of the group of enzymes specified by the operon. The structural genes belonging to the same operon generally determine the composition of enzymes that catalyze a sequence of biochemical reactions. On reflection, this feature of operons makes sense, so to speak. If a chain of biochemical reactions is to be turned on or off in the cell by controlling the synthesis of one or more of the necessary enzymes, it is economical to initiate, or to halt, the synthesis of the *entire* group of enzymes, lest an enzyme be produced, at the expense of energy and raw materials, when it can serve no function whatsoever. The role of genes in the metabolic economy of the cell and in the regulation of biosynthetic activity thus stands revealed in its beautiful complexity and order.

CHAPTER VI

THE FUTURE OF GENETICS: TODAY'S UNSOLVED PROBLEMS

The last two decades have witnessed breathtaking progress in the science of genetics, progress resulting primarily from investigation, at the molecular level, of hereditary material, its structure, and activity. Success at this level of research has, indeed, been so remarkable that one is led to wonder whether all of the fundamental problems posed by classical genetics have received a definitive solution. This is a convenient point, therefore, to retrace our steps and reconsider the questions that were posed at the end of the first chapter dealing with the legacy of classical genetics.

Proceeding into the 1940's it seemed important to know what the gene was in physical terms, to lift the veil off the gene as a purely formal, abstract unit of inheritance as revealed in biparental crosses, and to determine its chemical structure. Knowing this structure, it seemed likely that geneticists would soon understand how genes control the development of the characters we recognize in an organism's phenotype. In retrospect, this molecular approach to the genetic material appears highly justified. The first step forward came from evidence that the nuclear genes were composed of deoxyribonucleic acid and that this substance carried genetic information. The next important leap forward was the proposal of Watson and Crick as to the structure of DNA. With this molecular model of the genetic material, it was possible to conceive how DNA might replicate, mutate, and become transcribed into RNA. The experimental verifications of the theoretical predictions were fast in coming and persuasive in their support of the model. Geneticists have now acquired a clear insight into the molecular basis of the properties of the genetic material.

The answer to the first question posed by classical genetics—what is the gene?—is fairly straightforward, once we are prepared to define the gene in a particular way. Having learned that the genetic units of recombination, mutation and heterocatalytic function do not coincide, we may adopt the arbitrary, but useful, convention of applying the term "gene" to the demonstrably largest of these units, the unit of heterocatalytic function. (This function would be equivalent to transcription if it were shown that all genes intervene in the cell's metabolism by being transcribed into complementary RNA structures.) The gene then becomes a specific segment of DNA (a specific sequence of deoxynucleotide pairs) that governs a specific biochemical reaction in the cell. The agency of government is presumably some macromolecular product specified by the gene's structure, and at least in some cases—those of the structural genes—the product is a complementary messenger RNA.

Do the answers to the remaining questions follow in a simple way? How, for example, does the gene act to control the development of the characters of a multicellular organism? The answer to this question is only partly satisfying. Accepting the view that the gene acts heterocatalytically by specifying the formation of some macromolecular product, it is possible to imagine numerous ways in which this product might intercede in the metabolic economy of the cell, and of the multicellular organism, and in so doing affect various phenotypic characters. Being able to imagine the possible intercessions of the gene's product is not equivalent, however, to demonstrating the occurrence of any one of them. At the present time, the situation may be described in the following way. If the character one is following in development is a biochemical reaction or a metabolic substance, one can trace rather easily the path from gene to the biochemical character. If, on the other hand, one is following so complicated a character as a wing, an eye, or a muscle, one must admit that the path from gene to character has not yet been clearly illuminated.

There were, of course, still other questions posed by classical genetics. How is the gene disposed on the chromosome, and how does intrachromosomal recombination, or "crossing-over" occur? How does the gene change and how does the genotype change in the course of evolution? Let us, then, consider all of these questions in turn.

The Genes and the Cytoplasm in Morphogenesis

The cell is hardly a loose assemblage of materials reacting in a random way to produce the energy and synthesize the macromolecules necessary for the cell's growth and reproduction. A detailed examination of the cell by biochemical fractionation and microscopy confirms us in this view. The substances of which the cell is composed are not only segregated between the nucleus and the cytoplasm, but there is a highly specific arrangement of materials within each of these principal areas of the cell (see Plate 5). The mitochondria are distinct in size, shape, and chemical composition from the ribosomes which, in turn, differ in these respects from the Golgi apparatus, the cytoplasmic membrane, and cell wall. There is good reason to believe that the order and regularity of biochemical processes depend on the structural organization of these cellular organelles.

If what has just been said about the organization of the cell is true, it is no less so about the multicellular organism. Much of the discussion in this book has concerned the microorganism (bacterium, yeast, or mold), which in many respects is equivalent to a single cell. But there is an important respect in which the cell of the multicellular organism differs from the unicellular microorganism. The micro-organism is, after all, an organism capable of all the metabolic processes characteristic of a living enterprise: energy production and transfer, macromolecular synthesis, metabolic regulation, reproduction, genetic transfer, and recombination. The cell of a multicellular organism is, most often, a specialized entity, capable of only a small part of the biochemical repertoire characteristic of the organism as a whole. We say that the cells of a multicellular organism are *differentiated* from each other precisely because they look and act differently. Regulation within the multicellular organism is usually the result of interactions between cells of different types.

How do the cells of a plant or an animal become differentiated in form and function? How, indeed, does the organism grow, change constantly in its internal construction, change in its outer form, and yet always maintain the integrity of a living organism? These have been the classic problems of the developmental biologist (or embryologist, as he was known in days of yore). Obviously, our current knowledge of genetics should make a powerful contribution to the solution of these problems, for the genes determine a great many of the biochemical reactions on which all complex developmental characters must depend. Indeed, the mutant genotypes studied by the classical geneticists obviously produced changes in such complex phenotypic characters as wing structure, pigment formation and distribution, and so on. Moreover, the classical studies revealed how complicated genic intervention was. Many different genes contributed to the development of the same complex phenotypic character, and a single gene might contribute to the development of different characters. This complexity need not deter the developmental biologist, however. Our present insight into the nature of gene action provides ways of conceptualizing the process of organismic development.

The demonstration of a category of regulator genes in bacteria, for example, throws some light on the problem of differentiation. The role played by regulator genes in the morphogenesis of higher plants and animals is not yet known, but an interesting insight is provided by the situation in bacteria, for it is clear that genes may not exert their heterocatalytic function at all times. The total potential represented in the genotype of an organism may not be expressed in every cell. Cells may be differentiated within the multicellular organism because the genes that are active or "silent" in one group of cells may not be the same active or silent ones in another group. Is there, in fact, a control of gene action within the cells of a multicellular organism? If so, is this control, in part or wholly, the result of regulator genes? In any case, what environmental differences, presumably internal to the organism, induce the activity of genes in one group of cells and silence on the part of the same genes in another group of cells? And how does such environmental partitioning come about? To what extent does genic activity in early stages of organismic development help to create the internal environmental pattern that will have still further effects on differentiation and morphogenesis?

Another interesting possibility is the existence of episomes in the fertilized egg. Episomes, it will be recalled, are recognized in bacteria as genetic determinants that follow two alternative regimes: either they are integrated into the bacterial chromosome, or they are replicated independently of the chromosome. They are, in either case, determinants that are not essential for the bacterium's survival and reproduction: they may be dispensed with, but they do add special properties to the cell when they are present. In the cell lineages derived from the early mitoses of the embryo, could there be first a switch from the integrated to the autonomous condition, and then a parceling out of several different kinds of episomes? Could this parceling out create differentiation? If so, what conditions specify the way in which the parceling out occurs, for development is not a haphazard affair, but is reproduced in an orderly way every generation?

Finally, we must return to the unsettled question of the role of the cytoplasm in hereditary transmission. Evidence has already been cited of mutational changes occurring within cytoplasmic structures, changes that are inherited and lead to mutant phenotypes. How much of the information for cellular differentiation and morphogenesis resides in cytoplasmic organelles? One may justifiably suspect that a great deal more does than has been demonstrated at the present time. An even more intriguing question issues from the results of recent research on nuclear transplantation. In this work, nuclei are removed from zygotes or differentiated cells, and they are transplanted either into zygotes or differentiated cells. Sometimes nuclei are transplanted into cells of different genic or chromosomal constitution than the ones from which they were isolated. The object of such studies is to determine whether nuclei are indifferent to the cytoplasm surrounding them or are, in fact, "conditioned" to some extent by the cytoplasm. Similarly, it is possible to discover whether the cytoplasm retains some autonomy in regard to its own differentiation or is at the mercy of whatever nucleus is introduced into its midst. While these recent investigations are far from unequivocal and conclusive at the present time, they do suggest that the nucleus is not the exclusive determinative influence of the cytoplasm's structure, and they suggest, moreover, that a specifically differentiated cytoplasm may alter the state of a zygote nucleus transplanted into it. In this latter respect, it is not clear whether the differentiated cytoplasm causes a gene mutation, or, as seems more likely, it induces some relatively long-lasting alteration in the genic activity within the nucleus. The interaction between nucleus and cytoplasm in the course of development appears to be complex, but then so is development. An interesting possibility is that the nuclear genes may determine the production of certain macromolecular constituents in the cytoplasm early in development, and that the stable cytoplasmic modification may "feed back" and repress (or induce) specific genes within the nucleus. Thus, given an initial differentiation in gene activity, subsequent waves of biochemical differentiation may result from a nuclear-cytoplasmic "feedback" or homeostatic mechanism. Our picture of the role of genes and cytoplasm in the development of a multicellular organism is lacking detail and clarity, but some new avenues of exploration have at least been indicated by the results of molecular genetics.

Behavior, an Aspect of Development

The most remarkable feature of the development of higher animals in that of behavior. In particular, we are intrigued by such facets of behavior as learning and memory. How does the mammal, for example, learn to perform complex locomotor operations in response to some environmental situation, operations that are not part of an inherited, instinctive pattern at birth? An artificial, experimentally contrived example would be the ability of rats to work their way through a maze with increasing efficiency, or the ability of rats to learn to ring a bell and switch off a light in order to obtain food.

Involved in learning is memory, the retracing of the steps by which a particular outcome was achieved in some prior experience of the animal. Memory, in turn, is the result of channeling impulses along a unique chain of nerve cells within a huge network of nerve cells. The conduction of an impulse from one nerve cell to the next has been shown to require a fairly intimate connection, or synapse, between the cells. Some of these synapses are built into the nervous system at time of birth, but many others are produced during the continuing experience of the organism. What processes fashion these synapses? What role does the hereditary apparatus, both nuclear and cytoplasmic, play in these processes?

An interesting suggestion has been made for a biochemical basis of memory, based on our new knowledge of the information potential in the structure of nucleic acids. This suggestion is that specific nucleic acids, most likely ribonucleic acids, are produced in certain nerve cells concomitantly with learning, and that these specific nucleic acids are fairly stable and represent a "trace" or "biochemical memory" of the neural channel associated with a particular, learned locomotor operation. This idea is little more than a provocative working hypothesis at the present time, but the analogy of memory to genetic information contained in this hypothesis may prove to be a fruitful stimulus to new kinds of research on the molecular basis of behavior.

However fruitful this idea may become, there is no doubt that the major problem of animal behavior remains that of the intricate organization of the nervous system. The sophisticated behavioral patterns of which the higher animals are capable, to say nothing of the patterns of intelligence and thought in mammals, involve integrated webs of nerve cells. How these integrated channels come to be developed and how their neural elements interact with each other remain largely unknown. Of course, an understanding of behavior is not a primary task of genetics, except insofar as an understanding of gene action in development comes to enlighten the behavioral side of development. In this regard, it is worth noting that a new field of biology has been created, one that weds psychology and genetics and goes by the name of "behavioral genetics."

DNA and the Chromosome

Classical genetics posed the fundamental problem: how is the gene disposed on the chromosome? The answer to this question, when focused on bacteria, has turned out to be fairly simple. The "chromosome" of the bacterium seems to be little more than a single, continuous molecule of DNA (see Plate 3). Moreover, this continuous stretch of DNA appears to be without ends, being cast in the form of a filamentous loop. It is only during the extraction of DNA from bacterial cells that this loop, having a molecular weight of over 10^9, is fractured into linear fragments having molecular weights, on the average, of 10^7. There is no evidence, at least in bacteria, that this loop of genetic material is interrupted periodically by material other than DNA, no evidence, in other words, that there are "spacers" of a non-DNA nature between genes. The problem remains as to how the individual functions inherent within the continuous stretch of DNA get sorted out. How does the gene-transcribing machinery know, for example, where one gene ends and another begins? As has been suggested previously, certain nucleotide triplets, or specific sequences of a longer nature, may code effectively as gene-separators; certain sequences may be read as indicating where one gene leaves off and another begins.

The problem of how the gene is disposed on the chromosome of an organism more advanced than a bacterium is not so simple, however. The reason is the complexity of the chromosome itself. The chromosome of the higher organism is large, and, at least during certain stages of the cell cycle, it is readily visible under the ordinary light microscope. (The bacterial chromosome, on the other hand, has only been rendered visible by electron microscopy or by autoradiography, both of which techniques permit one to make out the outlines of the DNA molecule.) Largely invisible between periods of mitosis, the plant or animal chromosome contracts, getting thicker and shorter during the mitotic process. At this time, after appropriate staining, the chromosome is easily observed with the light microscope. The large size of the plant and animal chromosomes is only partly due to the greater number of genes contained in them than in bacterial chromosomes. The plant and animal chromosome owes much of its size to its considerable chemical complexity. It is not composed solely of DNA, as is apparently the case with the viral and bacterial chromosome; it contains, in addition, ribonucleic acids and proteins of several kinds. Indeed, most, if not all, of the nucleic acids can be removed without appreciably affecting the morphological integrity of the chromosomes. The residual protein forms a structure having most of the structural landmarks of the original chromosome. Obviously, the chemical organization of the chromosomes of higher organisms is complex, and our knowledge of the relationship of the various macromolecular constituents to each other in the intact chromosome is quite sketchy. It is not even certain that DNA forms a continuous molecule along the length of the chromosome in higher organisms. If, indeed, the chromosomal DNA were interrupted by materials of a non-DNA nature, the independent transcription of the genes in higher organisms could be understood.

One fact is known, however, that is of importance in understanding the structure of the complex chromosome of higher organisms. This fact derives from the elegant studies of J. Herbert Taylor and his colleagues. In brief, Taylor caused plant chromosomes to incorporate tritiated thymidine into their DNA. Thymidine is, of course, a nucleoside which is built into the DNA double helix. In this way, the chromosomes come to be labeled with tritium, and they can then be autoradiographed (see Chapter II, page 72). The same chromosomes can also be viewed with the light microscope, and their form observed by this method can be compared with that in the autoradiographs. The chromosomes, immediately after incorporation of radioactive thymidine, are seen as uniformly labeled structures. If the chromosomes are allowed to replicate once in a medium containing nonradioactive thymidine, they appear to contain two linear subunits, one labeled and the other unlabeled. If still another round of replication is permitted, two types of chromosomes are observed, one completely unlabeled and the other half-labeled as in the previous generation. These experimental results demonstrate that DNA of plant chromosomes replicates semiconservatively, as it does in bacteria and viruses. Moreover, the DNA is arranged in plant chromosomes in such a way that its subunits are segregated into the daughter chromosomes produced by mitosis. Following the work of Taylor's group, similar findings have also been made for the DNA of mammalian chromosomes, including those of humans. These findings obviously restrict the number of models that may be postulated for the structure of the chromosomes of higher organisms, but it still leaves open a number of possibilities that need to be examined in future investigations.

A basic protein is closely associated with DNA in the chromosomes of plants and animals. The common basic proteins are the histones and protamines, and owe their basic properties to their relatively high content of the basic amino acids arginine and lysine. There are apparently several different kinds of histones, differing from each other in their exact amino acid content. Histones differ in the various cells of a multicellular organism, and they may also be seen to vary in the differentiation of a single group of cells. Thus, the chromosomal histones change as sperm cells mature from their relatively undifferentiated state immediately following meiosis (when they are called spermatids), to the state in which they are capable of fertilization (when they are called spermatozoa). In spermatids, the predominant basic protein is a histone rich in lysine, whereas in spermatozoa it is replaced by a protamine rich in arginine. Such change in the basic proteins is often associated with functional change, and for this reason the basic proteins are believed to have some part in gene activity. One current theory is that the basic proteins, especially the histones, control genic activity by suppressing the transcription of those genes to which they are attached; "histone-free" genes are the active ones, according to this idea. Our present knowledge of differential chromosome activity is not advanced far enough, however, to permit discrimination between this possibility and the equally tenable hypothesis that the histones change (in type and in distribution) *after* the genes do—that, in fact, the histones are part of the manifestation of gene activity, not the controllers of it.

The chromosomes are unusual in certain tissues of higher organisms. In the salivary glands of certain fly larvae (in-

cluding those of the fruit fly *Drosophila*), the chromosomes
are extraordinarily increased in both length and width (see
Plate 6). These "giant" salivary gland chromosomes lend
themselves well to studies of chromosomal structure and
gene activity. Unfortunately, we still do not have a very
clear idea of the structure of giant chromosomes, although
it seems that at least part of their increased width is due
to the increased number of DNA strands in these chromosomes (the strands apparently having been replicated without separating). Despite this basic ignorance of the structure of giant chromosomes, certain interesting findings have
been made. Because of the large size of the salivary gland
chromosomes, local changes are readily discernible. In some
fly species, the salivary gland chromosome exhibits "puffs"
at specific places and at specific times in larval development.
These "puffs" are composed of DNA or RNA, and they are
due to nucleic acid synthesis in localized regions of the
chromosome. There are important questions that still need to
be answered. What factors cause such differential nucleic
acid synthesis? How can DNA be replicated in one part of the
chromosome without concomitant DNA replication in the
remainder of the same chromosome? What connection is
there between development and differential nucleic acid
synthesis? Is it a causal connection, and if so, in which
direction: developmental change → differential nucleic acid
synthesis, or differential nucleic acid synthesis → developmental change?

Another important property of the complex organization
of the chromosome of higher organisms is coiling. As already
mentioned, the chromosome contracts during mitosis or
meiosis as a result primarily of coiling. Some regions of the
chromosome, however, coil somewhat earlier than others,
so that, during the early stage of mitosis or meiosis, intensely
coiled regions, or chromomeres, are seen distributed along
the chromosomal length. Indeed, some regions of the chromosome remain in a coiled state over very long periods of
time, and even through interphase, the so-called "resting

period" between mitoses. These persistently coiled pycnotic regions stain more intensely with basic dyes, and therefore are readily visible as dark masses or blobs within the stained nucleus. It is not clear what intracellular conditions induce coiling, although it is now known that the pycnotic state is associated with gene inactivity. Thus, genes in a highly condensed, coiled region of the chromosome are often inactive. For example, in female mammals, which have two X chromosomes, one of the X chromosomes becomes pycnotic in every somatic cell. Genes in the pycnotic X chromosome are inactive. (Interestingly enough, it is not always the same X chromosome that undergoes pycnosis in every somatic cell. Therefore, in females heterozygous for genes on the sex chromosome, the somatic cells are a phenotypic mosaic. In some cells, one sex-linked allele is active, in other cells the other sex-linked allele is active. The female cells are effectively haploid for the X chromosome, just as the male cells are, although the female body is a mosaic in this regard, unlike the male body.) Moreover, as is further discussed below, a fragment of the X chromosome may become translocated into an autosomal (nonsex) chromosome. When such a translocation occurs, the translocated X fragment may become pycnotic, as it would under nontranslocated conditions. The interesting effect is observed, however, that autosomal genes adjacent to the translocated X fragment are rendered inactive when pycnosis occurs. The inactivation of autosomal genes may spread for some distance from the region of the X translocation. Examples from other organisms are known in which pycnotic regions of the chromosome (sometimes referred to as "heterochromatin"), when translocated to new positions, inactivate the genes next to which they come to reside. The inactivating influence of the pycnotic region is not understood, but it might be due to some change in the association of DNA with some other component of the chromosome (possibly histones), resulting in repression of the DNA's heterocatalytic activity. Nor is it known whether genic repression by pycnosis plays an important part in the development of the organism.

One important avenue of cytogenetic research in the future is obvious. It will be concerned with the structure and function of the chromosome of higher organisms, with the structure and function of its constituent parts, and of their relation to development.

Recombination, Crossing-over, and Chromosomal Rearrangements

Another question posed by classical genetics concerned recombination between linked genes. An important distinction bearing on this question resulted from advances in molecular genetics. One must now distinguish, at least in principle, between recombination of nucleotide sites belonging to homologous DNA molecules and recombination of loci belonging to homologous chromosomes. (Here and throughout the remainder of this chapter we will be referring to the complex chromosomes of plants and animals.) From the considerations discussed in the preceding section, we realize our ignorance of the organization of DNA within the chromosome. In particular, we simply do not know whether DNA runs continuously along the length of the chromosome or is interrupted by regions composed of material other than DNA. Consequently, recombination within the chromosome of the higher organism may be conceived to occur in two ways. The first of these ways is the kind of recombination that can take place within the limits of the DNA molecule itself. The second could be a process of crossing-over involving the non-DNA portions of the chromosome. This is not to conclude that two distinct processes of recombination do occur at the level of the chromosome. The present state of our knowledge simply cannot rule out the possibility of two modes of intrachromosomal recombination. Thus, an additional advantage to be gained from a combined chemical and genetic analysis of the chromosome will be a resolution of this issue: can the recombination known to take place within the DNA molecule account for all the features of chromosomal "crossing-over?"

Perhaps this last question cannot be definitely answered until we are really sure how recombination between DNA molecules takes place. In Chapter IV, the difficulties in settling this problem were presented. In brief, biochemical evidence makes quite unequivocal the conclusion that molecular recombination involves breakage of DNA molecules. This breakage is followed by the union of fragments, so as to produce new combinations of the original ("parental") molecules. Nevertheless, certain features of intragenic recombination are not simply explained by such breakage and reunion. In particular, nonreciprocal recombination ("gene conversion") and negative interference are more readily understood by a model presuming "switching" between alternative parental templates during replication. It is not ruled out, of course, that *both* breakage-reunion and copy-choice are involved in molecular recombination. If copy-choice did occur, it would have to be limited to very short regions of the chromosome, to lengths no larger (and perhaps smaller) than those of genes themselves. Breakage-reunion would account for the characteristic features of crossing-over involving distances larger than those of genes, and the limited form of copy-choice would account for the special features of recombination within the boundaries of a gene. Recombination at the molecular level is, therefore, not yet completely understood, although future experimentation is confidently expected to clarify the situation since the physicochemical techniques necessary for the task are at hand.

Homologous chromosomes undoubtedly break, and the ends of the fragments rejoin in new ways, when new combinations are produced of parentally contributed genes. Chromosomal breakage is not restricted, however, to the phenomenon of crossing-over. The sensitivity of the chromosome to breakage in a plane perpendicular to its long axis is revealed in other phenomena as well. As was pointed out in Chapter I, nonhomologous chromosomes may break and exchange fragments during the healing process. Such transfer of a block of genes from one chromosome to a different one in the chromosomal complement of the cell is called *translocation*. This process is especially stimulated by the passage of ionizing radiation through chromosomes. Translocations obviously alter the linkage relationships of genes. A block of genes, X, that used to be linked to a block Y and unlinked to a block Z may, as a result of translocation, become unlinked to Y and linked to Z. Translocations thus bring whole groups or complexes of genes into new associations. A consequence of such changes on gene action has already been mentioned. Translocations are not the only outcome, however, of chromosomal breakage. A rearrangement of genes also comes about when two breaks occur at more or less distant points on a chromosome and the interstitial region turns 180° and heals to the distal regions in this new orientation. In this way, *inversions* of parental gene sequences may occur. Inversions also result in new neighborhoods for certain genes, specifically for those genes adjacent to the breakage points. Finally, it is known that a gene, or a block of genes, may drop out of a chromosome, and thus cause a deficiency or *deletion* in the chromosome. Such a deletion may be the result of two breaks in the chromosome, with the interstitial region dropping out and being permanently discarded as the broken ends of the chromosomes join and heal. Interestingly enough, *duplications* of genes, or of gene blocks, are also known. Duplications are believed to come about as a result of rare misalignments of homologous chromosomes during meiotic synapsis. Cross-overs between such mispaired chromosomes result in a reciprocal duplication and deficiency; that is, one chromosome has a duplicated region, whereas the homologue has suffered a deletion of that region.

What is the cause of chromosomal breakage? Perhaps one should say *causes*, for there may be more than one way in which a chromosome breaks. Everything may not be known about chromosomal breakage when we understand the mechanism of DNA breakage and recombination, for, as has been stressed previously, the chromosome of the higher organism is more than DNA, and breakage of the non-DNA portions of the chromosome may have a lot to do with the forms of chromosomal breakage that have just been discussed.

What, moreover, causes homologous chromosomes to pair? What are the forces that bring chromosomes containing similar sequences of genes into the exquisitely matched alignments characteristic of meiotic synapsis? By meiotic synapsis is meant that period during meiosis when homologous chromosomes come to lie in close proximity to each other, and in such a fashion that homologous regions are directly opposite each other all along the lengths of the chromosomes. There is good recent evidence to believe that this pairing of homologous chromosomes is not the same as the pairing that allows genetic recombination to occur. The latter, or exchange pairing, is believed to precede the former, which may have to do with the segregation of homologous chromosomes during meiosis. Indeed, exchange pairing may differ in still another respect from segregational pairing; at a given moment, exchange pairing may occur only at restricted, highly localized regions of the homologous chromosomes, instead of involving their entire lengths as is the situation in segregational pairing. Exchange pairing may, in fact, occur at such an early time in meiosis that the chromosomes are still invisible (at least under the light microscope); the pairing that *is* observed in meiosis may well be segregational pairing, an event that has already been preceded by the physical exchanges between chromosomes which results in genetic recombination. If this view is correct, whatever is learned about recombination between DNA molecules may throw no light on segregational pairing of chromosomes. This problem has been raised here primarily to point out that we are still far from

a thorough understanding of the events underlying hereditary transmission.

Mutation, Chromosomal Rearrangements, and Evolution

The model of DNA structure proposed by Watson and
Crick has been extensively confirmed by subsequent experimentation. One of the model's great achievements is in explaining mutations. The conception of a transition from an
adenine-thymine pair of nucleotides to a guanine-cytosine
pair (or conversely, from a guanine-cytosine pair to an
adenine-thymine pair) accounts nicely for the so-called
point mutation. This is the mutation that may involve a
single nucleotide pair within the entire length, presumably
thousands of nucleotide pairs, constituting the gene. Work
with chemical mutagens, such as 5-bromouracil, 2-amino-
purine, and nitrous acid, has verified this conception to a
large extent. Nevertheless, there are still some open matters.
What about the multi-site mutation, for example? This is a
mutation extending over several mutable sites, as revealed
by recombinational analysis. Some multi-site mutations may
be deletions of genetic material, but it is unlikely that all
are of this nature. Do some multi-site mutations consist of
an extended change in nucleotide sequence, and if so, what
physicochemical mechanism brings them about? The molecular basis of mutation has a firm foundation; it may gain
further support and extension in the near future.

Changes in the nucleotide sequence of DNA occur spontaneously in all living organisms, and are probably no
different in their chemical origin than those produced de-
liberately by the scientist and his bag of physical and
chemical mutagens. Spontaneous mutations undoubtedly
arise because of the dynamic interplay between the organism and its environment. Metabolic accidents do happen;
analogues of bases found in nucleic acids do get into an
organism's food supply or are occasionally synthesized by
error in the living cell; ionizing radiation does traverse

cellular constituents from time to time, as a result of exposure to natural sources of radioactivity. These and other "accidents" assure a source of mutational change in all organisms.

The significance of such change is, of course, the raw material it offers to evolution. Indeed, any alteration of the hereditary potential, the genetic information contained in an organism, may conceivably be utilized in biological evolution. Changes in genetic information will come about not only through localized nucleotide changes within DNA, but also through gross chromosomal aberrations, such as the translocations and inversions discussed above. Among other effects, these transpositions bring large blocks of genes into new neighborhoods. The altered neighborhood is known to have an effect on the mutability of the transposed genes, and it also sometimes influences the expression of the transposed genes. Thus, the precise manner in which genes act depends on the larger gene complex in which they reside.

Deficiencies and duplications are also important as materials for evolution. Loss of genes, and loss of specific functions, may be one way in which one species may become differentiated from another. Duplications of genetic material are perhaps even more interesting from an evolutionary point of view. What initially may be a mere repetition of certain genes within the genetic constitution of an organism may lead, eventually, to an increase in the genetic repertoire of an organism. The additional genes are, in a manner of speaking, "free" to differentiate by mutation from their exact copies, and in so doing acquire new functions, especially if transposed into new neighborhoods. The unlinked "α" and "β" genes specifying the similar, but not identical, α and β chains of mammalian hemoglobin are believed to have diverged in this way. Thus, genetic duplication lends itself to increase in complexity, which is a feature of biological evolution.

Today evolutionary genetics is experiencing a merited revival of interest. Some of the most exciting new work is going on at opposite poles of biological investigation. On the one hand, the molecular level of evolution is being studied, and on the other hand, the complex dynamics of genetic shifts within populations is being analyzed. Although for the moment the strategies of research at the molecular and populational levels are being worked out in near independence, discoveries at the two levels may prove to have mutually stimulatory effects.

To the student of species diversity and change, it has long been obvious that the biological species is by no means genetically uniform. In the actual world in which organisms live, populations of organisms belonging to the same species are often spatially separated from each other. These different populations of the same species possess many genetic similarities, but they are not genetically identical. Within a given population, moreover, the individual organisms are not all genetically alike. These genetic differences are manifested in phenotypic differences affecting the behavior, gross anatomical appearance, physiology, and cellular metabolism of the organism—phenotypic differences that may be collectively referred to as the polymorphism of the population and of the species. This polymorphism is partly stable and partly dynamic, for at least some part of the phenotypic differences attributable to genetic differentiation is in a state of flux. Cyclic changes in the environment, or environmental trends, are correlated with corresponding shifts in the polymorphism of the natural population. It seems reasonable to the human observer that these shifts in the prevalence of certain genotypes within populations are elements of the larger evolutionary process operating in the biological universe; they are perhaps microcosmic events within the macrocosmic sweep of biological evolution. For this reason, genetic studies of natural populations in their ecological niches have taken on new interest, particularly as models amenable to quantitative manipulation and experimental tests are being constructed by the

modern ecologist and evolutionary geneticist. The populational level of biological research may soon have its
heyday.

At the other end of the investigational spectrum, studies
of the fine structure of the nucleic acids and proteins are
being conducted on different species of organisms. The
point of these studies is to reveal the extent to which macromolecular structure mirrors evolutionary divergence between species. Similarity in structure would be expected to
be more extensive in the macromolecules of species having
closer phylogenetic relationship. In advanced plants and
animals, the amount of DNA per haploid nucleus is much
greater than that in the bacterial nucleoid. Moreover, DNA
extracted from plant and animal cells is quite heterogeneous
in respect to the nucleotide content of the molecules (or
molecular fragments); there is also considerable overlap in
the relative amounts of guanine and cytosine found in the
DNA's of different plants and animals. In a given bacterial
species, however, the guanine + cytosine content of extracted DNA is remarkably uniform; this intraspecific
homogeneity of bacterial DNA is contrasted by wide differences in the nucleotide content of DNA's obtained from
different bacterial species. Yet, the greater the taxonomic
closeness between two bacterial species (the greater the
number of characters they share), the more similar are
their DNA's. This similarity in DNA structure is revealed
not only in similarity in the over-all nucleotide composition
(although perhaps not in exact nucleotide sequence), but
also in the ability of two specific DNA's to form "hybrid"
structures in renaturing after heat-denaturation, as well as
in the ability of parts of the respective DNA's to undergo
genetic recombination during interspecific transformation.
Nucleotide composition (and eventually nucleotide sequence, when this can be determined in DNA molecules),
"hybridization," and genetic recombination are tests, then,
of the genetic homology between organisms and species.

A molecular trace of the evolutionary divergence between species is at hand.

The exact amino acid sequences have been determined of proteins performing similar functions in different species. The results of such analysis have substantiated the concept that macromolecular structure reflects evolutionary difference. A protein that has been thoroughly investigated is hemoglobin. This oxygen-transporting protein of the red blood cell is found in all vertebrates. In most vertebrates, hemoglobin is a tetramer, made up of two α polypeptides and two β polypeptides. The amino acid sequences of both the α and the β polypeptides are well known. In comparing the α polypeptide of gorilla hemoglobin with that from a human, one finds a very striking resemblance; the two polypeptide chains differ in only two of their amino acids. This small difference is accentuated by the fact that a single amino acid difference may arise by mutation in the α chain of hemoglobin. The α chain of human hemoglobin differs, however, in 17 of its amino acids from the same chain of horse hemoglobin. This finding is, of course, not surprising, in view of the greater evolutionary closeness of man and the gorilla than of either of these species and the horse. Changes in protein structure undoubtedly accumulate with evolutionary time, so that the further two species have been separated by the evolutionary process, the greater the number of amino acid differences that would be encountered in their similarly functioning proteins. These amino acid differences would, of course, derive from differences in the nucleotide sequences of the structural genes affecting the similar proteins in the two species. Another protein that has been extensively analyzed is cytochrome c, which is a respiratory enzyme found in many species of living organisms from bacterium to human. The same general picture is obtained from the findings with this protein. Mammalian and avian cytochrome c are more similar to each other than they are to fish cytochrome c, and they show the least similarity to yeast cytochrome c. Evolution has left its mark even in proteins performing quite similar functions in different species.

Another interesting question is being tackled today. Is the DNA-RNA-protein code a universal one among living organisms, or does the genetic code itself change in the course of evolution? The evidence thus far suggests that the code is a conservative one. The messenger RNA of one species may be utilized by the protein-synthesizing ribosomal system of an unrelated species, and a protein is made characteristic of the species from which the messenger RNA was extracted. Therefore, the messengers produced by one species can be read by the protein-synthesizing machinery of another, quite unrelated species. The RNA-protein code thus appears to be universal. Universality of the DNA-RNA code is indicated by other experiments. As discussed in Chapter III, bacterial fertility factors ($F+$) may sometimes harbor bacterial genes. These sexducing particles may invade bacteria of the same and different species. When they infect different bacterial species, the transferred genes are transcribed as though they were in their original species. Clearly, there seems to be but one code among bacteria. Recently, moreover, it has been found that DNA of two quite different viruses that normally infect mammals may invade a species of bacterium known as *Bacillus subtilis*. One of these viruses is the vaccinia virus, which causes smallpox in man; the other is the polyoma virus, which is associated with cancerous growth in human tissues. DNA has been extracted from these viruses and placed in the environment of *B. subtilis* cells especially competent to accept and be transformed by DNA from bacteria of their own species. A sufficient amount of the human viral DNA gets into the bacteria to permit proteins characteristic of the mature viruses to be made. Obviously, *Bacillus subtilis* organisms can decipher the code of viruses that ordinarily carry out their genetic functions in mammalian cells. The universality of the genetic code has implications for our ideas about evolution. Evolution seems to have proceeded in such a way that the genetic code elaborated in ancient geological times has persisted in essentially its primitive state. The richness of biological diversity would appear to be manifold variations on a common theme.

Concluding Argument

The science of genetics has undergone a rapid development. The classical period was instrumental in revealing the order and regularity of hereditary transmission, in demonstrating the cellular processes underlying this regularity, but most important of all, it posed, in clear fashion, the kinds of questions requiring solution for further advance. These questions stimulated the quest for the chemical basis of heredity. The results were an extremely fruitful mixture of brilliant molecular theory and exhilarating experimental verification. Elucidation of the molecular level of genetic phenomena has been considerable: Replication, mutation, heterocatalytic function, and recombination of the genetic material are fairly well understood, at least in their main outlines.

The prospect for the future would seem to be a quest for the continuity between the molecular level of genetic organization and the events transpiring at the cellular, organismic, and populational levels. The future geneticist will seek the connection between the gene and the complex chromosome, between the gene and cell structure, between the gene and morphogenesis, and between the gene and the evolving population. A science has not blossomed and died as a result of the vigorous pursuits and conquests at the molecular frontiers; it has been reinvigorated by its contacts and extensions into the upper domains of biology concerned with supramolecular organization, with development, and evolution. The most difficult areas of genetic inquiry are perhaps yet to begin; they may prove to be the most interesting.

REFERENCES

Chapter I

Herskowitz, I. H. 1962. "Genetics." Little, Brown and Co., Boston, Massachusetts.—*A textbook for a modern college course in genetics.*

Levine, R. P. 1962. "Genetics." Holt, Rinehart and Winston, New York.—*A condensed survey of modern genetics, excluding evolution.*

Sturtevant, A. H., and Beadle, G. W. 1962. "An Introduction to Genetics." Dover Publications, Inc., New York.—*Reprinted essentially unchanged from the original publication by W. B. Saunders Co., summarizing how the field of genetics looked in 1939.*

Chapter II

Avery, O. T., MacLeod, C. M., and McCarty, M. 1944. Studies on the chemical nature of the substance inducing transformation of pneumococcal types. I. Induction of transformation by a deoxyribonucleic acid fraction isolated from pneumococcus type III. *Journal of Experimental Medicine* 79: 137–158.—*The classic paper demonstrating the capacity of DNA to carry genetic information.*

Campbell, A. M. 1962. Episomes. *Advances in Genetics,* 11: 101–145. —*A review of episomes, including an original theory of the manner in which episomes interact with chromosomes.*

Hayes, W. 1964. "The Genetics of Bacteria and Their Viruses." John Wiley and Sons, New York.—*A comprehensive treatise for the advanced student.*

Hershey, A. D., and Chase, M. 1952. Independent functions of viral protein and nucleic acid in growth of bacteriophage. *Journal of General Physiology* 36: 39–56.—*Experimental evidence that bacteriophage DNA initiates bacteriophage synthesis in the bacterial host.*

Jacob, F., and Wollman, E. L. 1961. "Sexuality and the Genetics of Bacteria." Academic Press, New York.—*A discussion of the authors' experiments, on which our current theory of bacterial conjugation and transduction is based.*

Ravin, A. W. 1961. The genetics of transformation. *Advances in Genetics* 10: 62–163.—*A comprehensive account of our present knowledge of DNA-induced genetic transformations.*

Stent, G. S. 1963. "Molecular Biology of Bacterial Viruses." W. H. Freeman and Co., San Francisco.—*A survey of the important knowledge gained through a study of bacteriophage.*

Chapter III

Beadle, G. W. 1945. Biochemical genetics. *Chemical Reviews* 37: 15–96.—*A review of the early evidence that genes control metabolic processes by directing enzyme synthesis.*

Benzer, S. 1957. The elementary units of heredity. *In* "Chemical Basis of Heredity," pp. 70–93. Johns Hopkins Press, Baltimore, Maryland.—*The divisibility of the gene, defined as a unit of function, as shown by a study of a particular class of bacteriophage mutants.*

Kornberg, A. 1961. "Enzymatic Synthesis of DNA." John Wiley and Sons, Inc., New York.—*A brief account of the early work on the enzyme polymerizing DNA.*

Meselson, M., and Stahl, F. M. 1958. The replication of DNA. *Cold Spring Harbor Symposia for Quantitative Biology* 23: 9–12.—*In a few pages are described the elegant experiments revealing the semiconservative reproduction of DNA.*

Pontecorvo, G. 1958. "Trends in Genetic Analysis." Columbia University Press, New York.—*An early discussion of fine structural analysis of the genetic material, and the consequences to our concept of the gene.*

Wagner, R. P., and Mitchell, H. K. 1964. "Genetics of Metabolism," 2nd ed. John Wiley and Sons, Inc., New York.—*A comprehensive treatise, for the graduate student, on the gene's role in metabolism.*

Watson, J. D., and Crick, F. H. C. 1953. The structure of DNA. *Cold Spring Harbor Symposia for Quantitative Biology* 28: 123–131.—*The authors discuss their model of DNA's structure and how it can account for replication and mutation.*

Chapter IV

Case, M. E., and Giles, N. H. 1958. Recombination mechanisms at the pan-2 locus in *Neurospora crassa. Cold Spring Harbor Symposia on Quantitative Biology* 23: 119–135.—*An example of nonreciprocal recombinations occurring within the gene.*

Krieg, D. 1963. Specificity of chemical mutagenesis. *Progress in Nucleic Acid Research* 2: 125–168.—*A critical review of current knowledge of the mechanism of chemically induced mutations.*

Meselson, M., and Weigle, J. J. 1961. Chromosome breakage accompanying genetic recombination in bacteriophage. *Proceedings of the National Academy of Sciences of the United States* 47: 857–868.—*Unequivocal evidence that bacteriophage recombination involves breakage and reunion of genetically dissimilar, "parental" DNA molecules.*

Voll, M. J., and Goodgal, S. H. 1961. Recombination during transformation in *Hemophilus influenzae*. *Proceedings of the National Academy of Sciences of the United States* **47**: 505–512.—*Linkage of a genetic marker introduced by transformation with a marker present in the host chromosome occurs very quickly and within a period of time in which no DNA synthesis can be detected.*

Chapter V

Brenner, S. 1961. RNA, ribosomes and protein synthesis. *Cold Spring Harbor Symposia on Quantitative Biology* **26**: 101–110.—*Evidence for a messenger RNA specified by bacteriophage DNA; the messenger utilizes pre-existing ribosomes in the infected bacterium for the production of bacteriophage proteins.*

Crick, F. H. C., Barnett, L., Brenner, C., and Watts-Tobin, R. J. 1961. General nature of the genetic code for proteins. *Nature* **192**: 1227–1232.—*A brilliant paper showing how much one can learn about the genetic code through a judicious use of proflavine-induced mutations and their suppressors.*

Hurwitz, J., Furth, J. J., Anders, M., Ortiz, P. J., and August, J. T. 1961. The enzymatic incorporation of ribonucleotides into RNA and the role of DNA. *Cold Spring Harbor Symposia on Quantitative Biology* **26**: 91–100.—*The role of DNA as a template in the enzymatically catalyzed production of RNA.*

Jacob, F., and Monod, J. 1961. Genetic regulatory mechanisms in the synthesis of proteins. *Journal of Molecular Biology* **3**: 318–356.—*How genes specifying the structures of bacterial enzymes are "switched on or off" by another class of genes; how the latter class of regulatory genes is activated by environmental agents of internal or external origin.*

Nirenberg, M. W., and Matthaei, J. H. 1961. The dependence of cell-free protein synthesis in *E. coli* upon naturally occurring or synthetic polyribonucleotides. *Proceedings of the National Academy of Sciences of the United States* **47**: 1588–1602.—*The enzymatically catalyzed incorporation of amino acids into protein is determined by the nucleotide composition of messenger RNA.*

Schlesinger, M. J., and Levinthal, C. 1963. Hybrid protein formation of *E. coli* alkaline phosphatase leading to *in vitro* complementation. *Journal of Molecular Biology* **7**: 1–12.—*A case of differently mutated forms of the polypeptide subunit combining to form a nearly normal enzyme.*

Spiegelman, S., and Hayashi, M. 1963. The present status of the transfer of genetic information and its control. *Cold Spring Harbor Symposium on Quantitative Biology* **28**: 161–182. *A review of cur-*

rent thinking as to how DNA controls the production of messenger, ribosomal, and transfer RNA.

Yanofsky, C., Carlton, B. C., Guest, J. R., Helinski, D. R., and Henning, U. 1964. On the colinearity of gene structure and protein structure. *Proceedings of the National Academy of Sciences of the United States* 51: 266–272.—*The positions of amino acid changes in tryptophan synthetase are related, in a colinear fashion, with the positions of mutations in the gene specifying that enzyme.*

Chapter VI

Anfinsen, C. B. 1963. "The Molecular Basis of Evolution." John Wiley and Sons, Inc., New York.—*In the final chapters of this book will be found an account of the evolution of protein structure during biological evolution.*

Briggs, R., and King, T. J. 1957. Changes in the nuclei of differentiating endoderm cells as revealed by nuclear transplantation. *Journal of Morphology* 100: 269–312.—*Do genes become permanently altered as a consequence of the differentiation of the cells containing them?*

Ephrussi, B. 1953. "Nucleo-cytoplasmic Relations in Microorganisms." Clarendon Press, Oxford.—*The significance of cytoplasmic mutations, and their interactions with nuclear mutations, on the general problems of cell heredity and differentiation.*

Ingram, V. M. 1963. "The Hemoglobins in Genetics and Evolution." Columbia University Press, New York.—*A great deal of what we know about the genetic control and evolution of protein structure has been gained from a study of mammalian hemoglobins and is summarized in this book.*

Moore, J. A. 1958. Transplantation of nuclei between *Rana pipiens* and *Rana sylvatica. Experimental Cell Research* 14: 532–540.—*Do genes become permanently altered as the consequence of a sojourn in a genetically foreign cytoplasm?*

Swanson, C. P. 1960. "The Cell." Prentice-Hall, Inc., Englewood Cliffs, New Jersey.—*An introduction to the structure, reproduction, and development of the cell, revealing some of the complexities of the dynamic organization of the living cell.*

Taylor, J. H., Woods, P. S., and Hughes, W. L. 1957. The organization and duplication of chromosomes as revealed by autoradiographic studies using tritium-labeled thymidine. *Proceedings of the National Academy of Sciences of the United States,* 43: 122–128.—*DNA is replicated and distributed semiconservatively during the reproduction of plant chromosomes.*

INDEX